M000007479

Writer's Workout
PRACTICE BOOK

Writer's Workout
PRACTICE BOOK

Program Author
Gretchen Bernabei

Appreciation

The Publisher gratefully acknowledges that ideas for the following lessons in this book have previously appeared in other works by Gretchen Bernabei and/or Barry Lane:

· Truths (pages 99–102), Idea Organizers (page 100–102), Kernel Essays (pages 100–102), Ba-Da-Bings! (pages 107–108), and Throwaway Writing (pages 127–128) are based on ideas in **Reviving the Essay** ©2005 by Gretchen Bernabei and published by Discover Writing Press.

· Get into an Argument (pages 103–105) and Ways You Know Things (pages 103–106) are based on ideas in **Why We Must Run with Scissors** ©2001 by Gretchen Bernabei and Barry Lane and published by Discover Writing Press.

· Snapshots and Thoughtshots (pages 115–116, 119–122), and Zero in on a Moment (pages 123–126) are based on ideas in **The Reviser's Toolbox** ©1999 by Barry Lane and published by Discover Writing Press.

Gretchen Bernabei and Barry Lane present open-enrollment seminars nationwide, and are available for in-service workshops with students and teachers. For more information, contact:

Discover Writing Press
1-800-613-8055
www.discoverwriting.com

Acknowledgments

Grateful acknowledgment is given to the authors, artists, photographers, museums, publishers, and agents for permission to reprint copyrighted material. Every effort has been made to secure the appropriate permission, but if any omissions have been made, please contact the Publisher.

COVER PHOTOGRAPH by Liz Garza Williams

PHOTOGRAPHS

Alamy Ltd.: p95 (drum ©Lebrecht Music and Arts Photo Library/Alamy).

Art Resouce: p47 (Day and Night by MC Escher/Art Resources, NY)

CORBIS: p34 (beach ©Martin Meyer/zefa); p61 (clerk ©Chuck Savage); p63 (hallway ©Randy Faris); p98 (break dancer ©image100); p99 (tennis player ©Joe McBride); p99 (student ©Gabe Palmer); p99 (bicycle ©Ariel Skelley); p107, 108 (flip flops ©Tim McGuire); p123 (mall); p123 (mountaineer ©Don Mason); p139 (tennis player ©Joe McBride); p181 (four firefighters).

Getty Images: p6 (teenager boys ©Tony Anderson/Taxi); p6 (girl with basketball ©Sean Justice/Photonica); p9 (teen pyramid ©Martin Sanmiguel/Taxi); p11 (carwash ©Yellow Dog Productions/The Image Bank); p31 (thunderstorm ©Jim Reed); p62 (teen driving test ©Cohen/Ostrow); p64 (two girls ©ColorBlind Images LLC); p69 (rollercoaster ©ATABOY); p70 (ice climbing ©Alan Kearney); p94 (yoga ©Red Chopsticks); p99 (family reunion ©Yellow Dog Productions/Taxi); p109 (friends ©Nancy Ney/Digital Vision); p109 (game controls ©Andrew Olney/Digital Vision); p110 (bride and groom ©Mel Curtis); p111 (bicycle ©PhotoDisc); p115 (starting line ©John Lund/Sam Diephuis/Blend Images); p134 (desert hiking ©Ken Chemus/Taxi); p134 (winning marathon); p155 (looking at map ©Yellow Dog Productions); p155 (trekkers enjoying view ©Gina Martin/National Geographic); p155 (four hiker ©Corey Rich/Aurora); p181 (airplane crew ©ColorBlind Images); p181 (cameraman ©Alan Pappe/Photodisc); p198 (spring in Vermont © Adams Jones/Getty Images).

JupiterImages: p32 (koi pond ©Alison Miksch/Botanica); p93 (DJ ©Wang Leng/Asia Images); p134 (teenage girl making breakfast in kitchen ©Rob Melnychuk/Brand X Pictures); p197 (teenage boy surfing ©Tom Servais/Workbook Stock/JupiterImages).

Masterfile: p6 (teenager girl ©Reid Lincoln Ashton/Masterfile).

PhotoEdit Inc.: p33 (concert band ©Tony Freeman); p116 (classroom ©Spencer Grant); p123 (teen girl and mother ©Mary Kate Denny); p123 (play ©Bob Daemmrich); p133 (mariachi band ©Jeff Greenberg); p140 (boarding school bus ©Michael Newman); p197 (teens arguing © Richard Hutchings/PhotoEdit).

SuperStock: p107, 108 (teenage boy ©Comstock/SuperStock).

ILLUSTRATIONS

Steve Björkman: p13
Samuel A. Minik: p103—105

© The Hampton-Brown Company, Inc.

All rights reserved. No part of this book may be reproduced or transmitted in any form or by any means, electronic or mechanical, including photocopying, recording, or by any information storage and retrieval system, without permission in writing from the Publisher.

National Geographic School Publishing
Hampton-Brown
P.O. Box 223220
Carmel, California 93922
800-333-3510
www.NGSP.com

Printed in the United States of America

ISBN 10: 0-7362-3381-4
ISBN 13: 978-0-7362-3381-1

07 08 09 10 11 12 13 14 15 9 8 7 6 5 4 3 2 1

Writer's Workout

PRACTICE BOOK

Contents

Chapter 1: The Writing Process

Get Some Ideas. 5
Choose Your Topic 8
Write for Different Audiences 9
Write for Different Purposes 11
Fill Out Your FATP Chart 13
Organize Your Ideas 14
Write Your First Draft 15
Gather Ideas: Put a Listener on It 17
Gather Ideas: Put Readers on It 18
Revised Draft 19
Tools: The Dictionary. 21
Tools: Personal Checklist 22
Correct Your Mistakes 23
Final Draft 25
Reflect on Your Writing 27

Chapter 2: Good Writing Traits

Focus and Unity 29
Central Ideas in Nonfiction. 31
Unstated Central Ideas 32
Central Ideas in Fiction 33
Central Ideas in Poetry 34
Focus Your Paragraphs 35
Focus Your Paper 37
Organization 39
Organize Your Paragraphs 41
Logical Order in Paragraphs 44
Chronological Order in Paragraphs 45
Cause and Effect in Paragraphs 46
Spatial Order in Paragraphs 47
Comparison and Contrast in Paragraphs 48
Problem and Solution in Paragraphs 49
Opinion and Support in Paragraphs 50
Getting Your Paragraph to Flow 51
Organizing an Essay: Prewriting 53
Organizing an Essay: First Draft 54
Organizing Your Essay: Revising 56
Development of Ideas. 57

© Hampton-Brown

Table of Contents, continued

Engage the Reader from the Start. 59

Develop Ideas in Nonfiction 61

Develop Ideas in Fiction. 63

Build Strong Conclusions 65

Voice and Style 67

Choosing the Right Voice 69

Choosing Effective Words 71

Add Color to Your Language: Similes. 73

Add Color to Your Language: Metaphors 74

Add Color to Your Language: Idioms 75

Add Color to Your Language: Pull It All Together. 76

Stay Active! 79

Avoiding Repetition 80

Vary Sentences: Beginnings and Types 81

Vary Your Sentences: Length 82

Join Neighboring Sentences 83

Join Sentences with Related Ideas. 84

Move the Details! 85

Use *Who, Whose, Which,* and *That* 86

Condense Ideas and Details 87

Written Conventions 89

Use Modifiers Carefully 91

Use the Right Word 92

Use Correct Punctuation 93

Use Complete Sentences. 95

Catch and Correct Mistakes 96

Chapter 3: Writing Clinic

Speak Your Truth 99

Explain Your Truth 100

Explain More Truths 101

Ways You Know Things 103

Prove It On Your Own 104

Ba-Da-Bing 107

Take Time for Transitions 109

Connect Your Paragraphs 111

Use the Intensity Scale 113

Add Snapshots and Thoughtshots. 115

Get on Target 117

© Hampton-Brown

Add Meat to the Bones 119
Zero In on a Moment 123
Take Out Throwaway Writing 127
Use Fewer Words 129
Write Tight 130
Vary Your Sentences 131
Spice Up Your Verbs 133
Add Details with Prepositions 135
Place the Modifier 136
Elaborate with Participles 137
Elaborate with Clauses 138
Elaborate with Absolutes 139
No More Boring Writing! 140

Chapter 4: The Many Writers You Are

Reflective Essay: Trap Family Memories 141
Reflective Essay: Analyze a Model 142
Plan a Reflective Essay 143
Reflective Essay: First Draft 145
Reflective Essay: Revised Draft 147
Letter of Problem Solving: Solve the Problem . . . 149
Letter of Problem Solving: Analyze a Model . . . 150
Plan a Letter of Problem Solving 151
Letter of Problem Solving: First Draft 153
Letter of Problem Solving: Revised Draft 154
Short, Short Story: Invent a Story 155
Short, Short Story: Analyze a Model 157
Plan a Short, Short Story 159
Short, Short Story: First Draft 161
Short, Short Story: Revised Draft 163
Persuasive Essay: What Do You Think? 165
Persuasive Essay: Analyze a Model 166
Plan a Persuasive Essay 167
Persuasive Essay: First Draft 169
Persuasive Essay: Revised Draft 171
Literary Critique: State Your Opinion 173
Literary Critique: Analyze a Model 174
Plan a Literary Critique 175
Literary Critique: First Draft 177

Table of Contents, continued

Literary Critique: Revised Draft 179
Résumé: Take Inventory 181
Résumé: Analyze a Model 182
Plan a Résumé 183
Résumé: First Draft 185
Résumé: Revised Draft 186
News Article: Gather Ideas for Reporting 187
News Article: Analyze a Model 188
Plan a News Article: Choose a Topic 190
News Article: Gather Information 191
News Article: Organize Information 192
News Article: First Draft 193
News Article: Revised Draft 195
Poem in Free Verse: Get Inspired 197
Poem in Free Verse: Analyze a Model 198
Plan Poem in Free Verse 199
Poem in Free Verse: First Draft 201
Poem in Free Verse: Revised Draft 202

Chapter 5: Research and Writing

Research Report: Develop a Game Plan 203
Information Sources: Plan Your Search 205
Selecting Print Sources 207
Evaluating Web Sites 209
Practice Paraphrasing 211
Practice Summarizing 213
Using Direct Quotes 215
Avoiding Plagiarism 216
Practice Synthesizing Ideas 217
Check for Focus 218
Develop an Outline 219
Practice Good Introductions 221
From Outline to Paragraphs 223
Practice Strong Conclusions 224
Integrating Ideas 225
Practice Citing Sources 227

© Hampton-Brown

Get Some Ideas

Check out the idea file on pages 5–7, and add some ideas of your own.

Quotations

"Friendship is a pretty full-time occupation if you really are friendly with somebody."

—Writer Truman Capote

"You can't shake hands with a clenched fist."

—Political Leader Indira Ghandi

_____

_____

_____

_____

_____

_____

_____

_____

_____

_____

_____

_____

_____

_____

_____

_____

_____

_____

_____

_____

Photos

Victorio and me

Get Some Ideas, continued

Topics

1. My best friend—my older brother Victorio _____

2. What I've learned about teamwork _____

3. What it means to be a true friend _____

_____

_____

_____

_____

_____

_____

_____

_____

_____

_____

_____

_____

_____

_____

_____

_____

Choose Your Topic

Use the graphic below to help you narrow down your topic.
Make it specific enough to cover in a couple of pages.

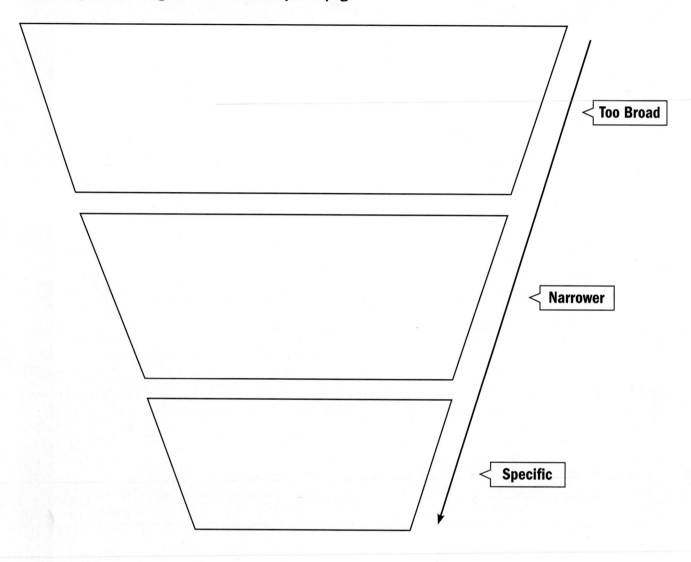

What, specifically, are you going to write about?
Describe how you plan to approach the topic.

_____

_____

_____

_____

_____

_____

_____

_____

_____

Write for Different Audiences

The person(s) for whom you're writing are your audience. Think of different audiences you might write for. Make them as different as possible. Add to this list.

my classmates _____ _____

my teacher _____ _____

_____ _____

_____ _____

_____ _____

Study the photo below. Choose three different audiences from the list above. On page 10, write one paragraph about the photo for each of the audiences you chose. How does your writing change?

1. Audience: _____

_____

_____

_____

_____

_____

_____

_____

_____

2. Audience: _____

_____

_____

_____

_____

_____

_____

_____

_____

_____

3. Audience: _____

_____

_____

_____

_____

_____

_____

_____

_____

_____

_____

Write for Different Purposes

What you hope to accomplish with your writing is your purpose. Think of different purposes for which you might write. Make them as different as possible. Add to this list.

to make my friends laugh

to tell my mother I appreciate her

Study the photo below. Choose three different purposes from the list above. On page 12, write one paragraph about the photo for each purpose you chose.

1. Purpose: _____

_____

_____

_____

_____

_____

_____

_____

_____

2. Purpose: _____

_____

_____

_____

_____

_____

_____

_____

_____

_____

_____

3. Purpose: _____

_____

_____

_____

_____

_____

_____

_____

_____

_____

_____

_____

Fill Out Your FATP Chart

Review page 8 to remember the topic you decided to write about. Choose an audience and purpose for your writing. Then go shopping for a form. Choose from the list below or one of your own.

FATP Chart

Form: _____

_____

Audience: _____

_____

Topic: _____

_____

Purpose: _____

_____

Writing Forms	Writing Advice	Writing Topics
Advice column	Essay	News story
Biography	Fable	Personal narrative
Book review	Flyer	Play
Business letter	Haiku	Poem
Cartoon	Invitation	Recipe
Character sketch	Journal entry	Research report
Comic strip	Letter to the editor	Résumé
Directions	Magazine article	Screenplay
Editorial	Movie review	Song lyrics
E-mail	Myth	

Organize Your Ideas

Shape your thinking using one of the graphic organizers from pages 30–37 of the *Good Writer's Guide*. Does the organizer go well with your purpose and your form?

Write Your First Draft

Use pages 15–16 to write your first draft.

NOTE: If you are writing your first draft on a computer, print out a hard copy and paste it on pages 15–16.

Checklist

- ❏ Use a title that tells what your writing is about.
- ❏ Get the reader's attention in your opening paragraph.
- ❏ Use your graphic organizer to write about ideas in an effective order.
- ❏ Support your ideas with enough details.
- ❏ Stick to your topic.

Gather Ideas: Put a Listener on It

Use pages 17–18 to reflect on your writing, gather feedback for revising, and plan what changes you'll make to your paper.

1. Read your paper to yourself. What parts sound good to you?

_____

_____

_____

_____

_____

_____

What parts need more work? Why?

_____

_____

_____

_____

_____

_____

2. Read your paper aloud to one peer and one adult. Ask some of the feedback questions that appear on page 53 of the *Good Writer's Guide*. Write down any answers you can use to revise your paper.

_____

_____

_____

_____

_____

_____

_____

_____

_____

Gather Ideas: Put Readers on It

1. Conduct a peer conference using the guidelines on page 54
of the *Good Writer's Guide.* Use the feedback you get to answer
these questions:

What's the best thing about your writing?

_____

_____

_____

What do you need to work on to improve your writing?

_____

_____

_____

What parts of your paper need to be re-organized, cut out,
or explained more fully?

_____

_____

_____

_____

What other changes did your reader suggest?

_____

_____

_____

_____

2. Now you're ready to decide how you will revise your paper.
Describe the changes you plan to make.

_____

_____

_____

_____

_____

_____

Revised Draft

Revise your first draft on pages on pages 15–16.
Write a clean copy of your revised draft on pages 19–20.

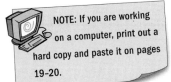

NOTE: If you are working on a computer, print out a hard copy and paste it on pages 19-20.

_____

_____

_____

_____

_____

_____

_____

_____

_____

_____

_____

_____

_____

_____

_____

_____

_____

_____

_____

_____

_____

_____

_____

Tools: The Dictionary

Edit the passage below. Use the dictionary excerpt at the bottom of this page.

Alex and I volunteered at the local aquarium two summers ago. As

I struggled to keep up with the fishes' feeding schedule, he exelled in

his duties. He enjoyed taking care of all of the animals at the aquarium

excepting for the sharks. He was really excitated and enjoyed the whole

experience. Now he is enrolled in a marine biology program at the

local community college. It is an exellant program.

---

exceeding • excommunicate 330

production〉. EXCEL implies preeminence in achievement or quality 〈*excelling* in athletics〉. SURPASS suggests superiority in quality, merit, or skill 〈the book *surpassed* our expectations〉. TRANSCEND implies a rising or extending notably above or beyond ordinary limits 〈*transcended* the values of their culture〉.

ex·ceed·ing \ik-'sēd-ing\ *adj* : exceptional in amount, quality, or degree 〈*exceeding* darkness〉

ex·ceed·ing·ly \ik-'sēd-ing-lē\ *also* **exceeding** *adv* : to an extreme degree : EXTREMELY 〈an *exceedingly* fine job〉

ex·cel \ik-'sel\ *vb* **ex·celled; ex·cel·ling** : to be superior : surpass in accomplishment or achievement 〈*excels* in mathematics〉 〈*excelled* her classmates〉 [Latin *excellere*, from *ex-* + *-cellere* "to rise, project"] **synonyms** see EXCEED

ex·cel·lence \'ek-sə-ləns, -sləns\ *n* 1 : the quality of being excellent 2 : an excellent or valuable quality : VIRTUE 3 : EXCELLENCY 2

ex·cel·len·cy \-sə-lən-sē, -slən-\ *n, pl* **-cies** 1 : outstanding or valuable quality — usually used in plural 2 — used as a form of address for a high dignitary of state (as a foreign ambassador) or church (as a Roman Catholic bishop) 〈Your *Excellency*〉

ex·cel·lent \'ek-sə-lənt, -slənt\ *adj* : very good of its kind : FIRST-CLASS — **ex·cel·lent·ly** *adv*

ex·cel·si·or \ik-'sel-sē-ər\ *n* : fine curled wood shavings used especially for packing fragile items [trade name, from Latin, "higher," from *excelsus* "high," from *excellere* "to excel"]

¹**except** *also* **ex·cept·ing** *prep* : with the exclusion or exception of 〈everybody *except* you〉 〈open daily *except* Sundays〉

²**ex·cept** \ik-'sept\ *vt* : to take or leave out from a number or a whole : EXCLUDE, OMIT [Medieval French *excepter*, from Latin *exceptare*, from *excipere* "to take out, except," from *ex-* + *capere* "to take"]

³**except** *also* **excepting** *conj* 1 : UNLESS 〈*except* you repent〉 2 : with this exception, namely 〈was inaccessible *except* by boat〉 3 : ³ONLY 2 〈I would go *except* it's too far〉

except for *prep* : with the exception of : but for 〈all A's *except for* a B in Latin〉

ex·cep·tion \ik-'sep-shən\ *n* 1 : the act of excepting : EXCLUSION 2 : one that is excepted; *esp* : a case where a rule does not apply 〈we'll make an *exception* this time〉 3 : an objection or a ground for objection 〈took *exception* to the remark〉

ex·cep·tion·able \ik-'sep-shə-nə-bəl, -shnə-\ *adj* : likely to cause objection : OBJECTIONABLE — **ex·cep·tion·ably** \-blē\ *adv*

er 5 : a place where things or services are exchanged: as **a** : an organized market or center for trading in securities or commodities 〈stock *exchange*〉 **b** : a central office in which telephone lines are connected to permit communication

²**exchange** *vt* 1 **a** : to give in exchange : TRADE, SWAP **b** : to replace by other merchandise 〈*exchange* this shirt for one in a larger size〉 2 : to part with for a substitute 〈*exchange* future security for immediate pleasure〉 — **ex·change·able** \-ə-bəl\ *adj* — **ex·chang·er** *n*

exchange rate *n* : the ratio at which the principal units of two currencies may be traded

exchange student *n* : a student from one country received into a school in another country in exchange for one sent to a school in the home country of the first student

ex·che·quer \'eks-ˌchek-ər, iks-'\ *n* 1 : the department of the British government concerned with the receipt and care of the national revenue 2 : TREASURY; *esp* : a national or royal treasury 3 : money available : FUNDS [Medieval French *escheker* "chessboard, counting table, exchequer," from *eschec* "check"]

¹**ex·cise** \'ek-ˌsīz, -ˌsīs\ *n* : an internal tax levied on the manufacture, sale, or consumption of a commodity within a country [obsolete Dutch *excijs*]

²**ex·cise** \ek-'sīz\ *vt* : to remove by cutting out 〈*excise* a tumor〉 [Latin *excisus*, past participle of *excidere* "to excise," from *ex-* + *caedere* "to cut"] — **ex·ci·sion** \-'sizh-ən\ *n*

ex·cit·able \ik-'sīt-ə-bəl\ *adj* : readily roused into action or an active state; *esp* : capable of activation by and reaction to stimuli — **ex·cit·abil·i·ty** \-ˌsīt-ə-'bil-ət-ē\ *n*

ex·ci·ta·tion \ˌek-ˌsī-'tā-shən, ˌek-sə-\ *n* : EXCITEMENT; *esp* : the activity or change in condition resulting from stimulation of an individual, organ, tissue, or cell

ex·cit·a·to·ry \ik-'sīt-ə-ˌtōr-ē, -ˌtȯr-\ *adj* : tending to produce or marked by usually physiological excitation

ex·cite \ik-'sīt\ *vt* 1 **a** : to call to activity **b** : to rouse to an emotional response **c** : to arouse (as an emotional response) by appropriate stimuli 2 **a** : ENERGIZE **b** : to produce a magnetic field in 3 : to increase the activity of (as nervous tissue) 4 : to raise (as an atom) to a higher energy level [Medieval French *exciter*, from Latin *excitare*, from *ex-* + *citare* "to rouse"] **synonyms** see PROVOKE — **ex·cit·er** \-'sīt-ər\ *n*

ex·cit·ed \-'sīt-əd\ *adj* : having or showing strong feeling : worked up 〈*excited* about the trip〉 — **ex·cit·ed·ly** *adv*

ex·cite·ment \ik-'sīt-mənt\ *n* 1 : the act of exciting : the state

---

Tools: Personal Checklist

Use page 22 to create your own personalized checklist of mistakes to watch out for.

1. Look back through your old papers to see which editing and proofreading errors are marked most frequently. Jot down your top 5 trouble-spots.

_____

_____

_____

_____

_____

2. Talk with your teacher about ways to fix these mistakes, or check out a style handbook for tips.

3. Now, create your personal checklist. List your most common mistakes and how you can fix them.

☑ Words I mix up:

• "you're" and "your"

"You're" is a contraction. Try substituting "you are" in the sentence to see if it still makes sense!

Correct Your Mistakes

Edit and proofread this passage. See how many grammar, spelling, punctuation, and capitalization errors you can find.

Editing and Proofreading Marks

∧	Insert something.
⋏	Add a comma.
⋏	Add a semicolon.
⊙	Add a period.
⊙	Add a colon.
⌄ ⌄	Add quotation marks.
⌄	Add apostrophe.
≡	Capitalize.
/	Make lower case.
℘	Delete.
¶	Make new paragraph.
=	Insert hyphen.
∼	Change order.
#	Insert space.
⌣	Close up.

One way my family members are alike is that they all express themselves carefuly. For example my grandpa Joe came here from Poland when he was 25. He could speak Polish Russian and German but he barley spoke English. However he was determined to learn. He used to go to his factery job during the day and study a Polish-English dictionary at night. Now he has a bigger vocabulary then anyone else I know.

Than there is my dad. He always uses language precisely and he make sure everyone around him does to. Suppose I ask him if I can drive drive his car. He will answer, Im sure your capable of driving it. Then he waits for me to ask, May I drive your car? Maybe my dad should of been an english teacher.

In my generation, their is my brother Dave who is apolice officer. He gets bored writing police reports that say things like, The car was hit by a garbage truck. So instead he will use a thesarus to write something like, The vehicle was struck by a municipal trash-collection unit. Dave says its just his way of making his job more interesting.

Edit and proofread this passage. See how many grammar, spelling, punctuation, and capitalization errors you can find.

Editing and Proofreading Marks	
∧	Insert something.
⋏	Add a comma.
⋏	Add a semicolon.
⊙	Add a period.
⊙	Add a colon.
⌄ ⌄	Add quotation marks.
⌄	Add apostrophe.
≡	Capitalize.
╱	Make lower case.
℘	Delete.
¶	Make new paragraph.
＝	Insert hyphen.
∩	Change order.
#	Insert space.
⌒	Close up.

Every year, my family gathers in a park near my house in San Francisco, CA. A whole cast of characters arrives my autns my uncles my cousins and my grandparents. My favorite Uncle, Federico drives a large recreational vehicle he travels constantly and he is a sales man. He always brings gift to me and my brother from different places. Then, there is my aunt Gabriella. She drives an old pick up truck that is older than I am. Aunt Gabriella owns a flower store in san diego. Its called Gabriellas Garden. She always brings bouquets bouquets of fresh cut flowers

One of the oldest members of my family is my grandfather Pedro. He is known for his giant green car and his excellent storytelling. It seems like every year my Grandfather always arrive last to make agrand entrance into the park. Better late than never, he always jokes My family puts on quite a show at our annual gatherings. The food is always good the music is festive and the games are competetive. I loook forward to seeing my relatives each year.

Go back now and carefully edit and proofread your revised draft on pages 19–20. Use editing and proofreading marks to show your changes.

Final Draft

Make a final copy of your writing, incorporating all of the corrections from pages 19–20.

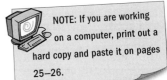

NOTE: If you are working on a computer, print out a hard copy and paste it on pages 25–26.

Reflect on Your Writing

Use pages 27–28 to reflect on what you've written for this chapter.

1. What surprised me about my writing?

_____

_____

_____

_____

_____

2. What unexpected questions or comments did I get from readers?

_____

_____

_____

_____

3. Which piece of writing makes me really proud? Why?

_____

_____

_____

_____

_____

4. In what ways have I become a better writer? What have I gotten really good at?

_____

_____

_____

_____

_____

5. What was the hardest writing assignment for me? Why?

_____

_____

_____

_____

_____

6. What are some areas of concern? How could I improve my work?

_____

_____

_____

_____

7. What piece of writing did I learn the most from? Why?

_____

_____

_____

_____

8. What did I discover about myself as I wrote?

_____

_____

_____

_____

9. What topics would I like to write about some more?

_____

_____

_____

_____

10. What other writing forms would I like to try? Why?

_____

_____

_____

_____

11. Does the essay I wrote for this chapter belong in my writing portfolio? Why or why not?

_____

_____

_____

_____

Focus and Unity

**Score the essay using the Writing Rubric on page 30.
Then answer the questions.**

Score	1	2	3	4

Electricity's in the Air

1   The next time there's a thunderstorm in your area, look outside your window. If you're really lucky, you might see one of these rare kinds of lightning—ball lightning, Saint Elmo's fire, or red sprites and blue jets.

2   Ball lightning, sometimes called globe lightning, is so rare that some scientists aren't sure it really exists. Then again, scientists also used to believe the Earth was flat, so what do they know? Witnesses report seeing small, often colorful glowing balls that occur near the ground during thunderstorms. The ball moves around and then suddenly disappears.

3   Saint Elmo's fire is another odd form of lightning. It's blue-green and often surrounds objects made of metal.

4   Personally, I love watching thunderstorms. Even as a child I found them fascinating. I've never seen colorful lightning, though. Red sprites and blue jets are very colorful forms of lightning which appear above storm systems. Both are usually very hard to observe but can sometimes be seen with the naked eye.

5   Lightning is really incredible when you think about it. I just don't understand how anyone could think that nature is boring. The natural world is just filled with amazing phenomena.

What's the topic?

_____

What is the central idea of the first paragraph?

_____

_____

Which details do not go with the main idea in paragraph 2? Delete them.

Fix paragraph 4 so all the details go with the main idea:

_____

_____

_____

Write a new conclusion that restates the central idea of the essay:

_____

_____

_____

_____

Focus and Unity

	How clearly does the writing present a central idea, opinion, or thesis?	How well does everything go together?
4 Wow!	The writing expresses a clear central idea or opinion about the topic.	**Everything in the writing goes together.** • The main idea of each paragraph goes with the central idea of the paper. • The main idea and details within each paragraph are related. • The conclusion is about the central idea.
3 Aaah.	The writing expresses a <u>generally</u> clear central idea or opinion about the topic.	**Most parts of the writing go together.** • The main idea of most paragraphs goes with the central idea of the paper. • In most paragraphs, the main idea and details are related. • Most of the conclusion is about the central idea.
2 Hmm.	The writing includes a topic, but the central idea or opinion is not clear.	**Some parts of the writing go together.** • The main idea of some paragraphs goes with the central idea of the paper. • In some paragraphs, the main idea and details are related. • Some of the conclusion is about the central idea.
1 Huh?	The writing includes many topics and does not express one central idea or opinion.	**The parts of the writing do not go together.** • Few paragraphs have a main idea, or the main idea does not go with the central idea of the paper. • Few paragraphs contain a main idea and related details. • None of the conclusion is about the central idea.

Central Ideas in Nonfiction

Turn the central idea into a thesis statement. Then use your thesis statement and appropriate details to write a paragraph that is focused and unified.

Central Idea: types of thunderstorms

Thesis Statement:

_____

_____

Details:

- There are several types of thunderstorms.

- Thunderstorms are categorized by "cells."

- One "cell" represents one updraft and one downdraft.

- Thunderstorms can be made of a single cell, multiple cells, or a supercell.

- Single-cell storms are often brief; multicell storms can last longer; supercell storms may last for hours.

- Supercell storms frequently produce hail and strong winds.

- Supercell storms sometimes develop into tornadoes.

Paragraph:

_____

_____

_____

_____

_____

_____

_____

_____

_____

_____

_____

_____

_____

_____

_____

_____

_____

Unstated Central Ideas

Read the letter below. Think about the writer's message. What is the unstated central idea?

Central Idea:

_____

_____

Finish writing the letter to go with the central idea, but without directly stating it.

_____ May 14, 2007

Dear Rosa,

  Last week, my family and I visited the Edmondson Nature Center for a workshop on building backyard ponds. I thought you might be able to offer us some advice since you are working at a fishery.

  After learning about various kinds of ponds, we decided to build a pond for Koi fish. My little sister, Heidi, really liked the huge size and various colors of the Koi. Luckily, there is a big, empty space in our backyard for the pond. We will be able to see it from the house, too.

_____

_____

_____

_____

_____

_____

_____

_____

_____

_____

_____

_____

_____

_____

_____

Central Ideas in Fiction

Write a paragraph about Kareem. Include details that develop the character and the situation in a way that fits the central idea.

Central Idea: Kareem may not be able to perform at the spring concert because of a storm

Details:

- It was the night of the spring concert at Central High.

- Kareem was nervous about performing tonight.

- The saxophone was invented around 1840 by Adolphe Sax.

- Kareem plays the saxophone for the school band.

- The band was setting up; Kareem's fellow band members were tuning their instruments.

- Kareem would like to learn how to play more songs on the saxophone.

- The weather forecast predicted thunderstorms and heavy rain.

- It was pouring rain when Kareem arrived at the school at 6:30 p.m.

- Suddenly, there was a loud thunderclap, and the power went out.

Paragraph:

_____

_____

_____

_____

_____

_____

_____

_____

_____

_____

_____

_____

_____

_____

_____

_____

_____

_____

Central Ideas in Poetry

Read the poem. What is the central idea?

Central Idea:

_____

_____

Underline details that help you find the central idea.

The Beach

Late in the afternoon
Sunbathers start to drift away
Fold up umbrellas and shake
Sand from blankets and towels.

Little kids stumble   5
Through the warm, damp sand towards home
Cheeks rosy from a day
Of salt water and sandcastles.

I stay for a while
Watching the sun sink   10
Quietly toward the horizon
Past the breaking waves.

Write a final stanza for the poem. Remember to add details that support the central idea.

_____

_____

_____

_____

_____

Focus Your Paragraphs

Add a topic sentence in the beginning and an appropriate detail in the middle of each paragraph.

1.

_____

_____

_____

Spring and summer are usually the best times to travel North America. People usually don't want to stay indoors when they are on vacation, and in spring and summer there are many opportunities for outdoor recreational activities.

_____

_____

_____

Many destinations, such as theme parks and beach towns, become very busy during this time of year, so travelers need to plan ahead.

2.

_____

_____

_____

Communication through the Internet has boomed since the late 20th Century. The Internet had previously been used by the high-tech industry. Nowadays, almost anyone can communicate through the Internet. _____

_____

_____

With the continual increase of Internet speeds as time goes on, the exchange of information over the Internet is becoming faster than ever.

Now add a topic sentence at the end and an appropriate detail in the middle of each paragraph.

3.

Studies show vending machines in most high schools are filled with candy, cookies, chips, soft drinks, and other sugary beverages. High school vending machines rarely sell fruits or healthy snacks. Considering around 30% of children are overweight, or at risk of becoming so, some schools have decided to rethink what's sold in vending machines. _____

_____

_____

In a recent survey, most students agreed that there should be healthier options in vending machines. _____

_____

_____

4.

The MP3 player is the most recently invented format for playing music. Records, eight-track tapes, cassette tapes, and CDs all led to the development of the MP3 format for playing music. MP3 players can hold thousands of songs and can be held in the palm of your hand. _____

_____

_____

With an MP3, a consumer can create personalized music lists and carry around thousands of songs. _____

_____

_____

Focus Your Paper

Use page 37 to plan a short essay. Be sure to create a strong central idea.

1. Opening Paragraph

Thesis Statement:

2. Paragraph 2

First Main Idea:

3. Paragraph 3

Second Main Idea:

4. Additional Paragraphs

Other Main Ideas:

5. Concluding Paragraph

Conclusion:

Focus Your Paper, continued

Use your plan on page 37 to write your essay.
Be sure to stay focused on the central idea.

NOTE: If you are writing your essay on a computer, print out a hard copy and paste it on page 38.

Focus and Unity Checklist

Draft

❑ Your thesis statement is clearly presented in the first paragraph.

❑ Each paragraph has a main idea that relates to the central idea.

❑ The details in each paragraph relate to the main idea.

❑ The conclusion revisits your thesis statement and sums up the main ideas in your essay.

Test your focus and revise

❑ Add a title.

❑ Add headings to each section or paragraph.

❑ Read them together to test your focus.

Organization

Score the essay using the Writing Rubric on page 40. Then answer the questions.

Score	1	2	3	4

A Web of Confusion

1 Ever since I was a kid, I've drawn cartoons—hundreds of them over the years. Last year I decided I wanted them to be seen by a wider audience. I decided to create a Web site to showcase my work. After all, millions of people have Web sites—how hard could it be to create one? Unfortunately, it was harder than I expected in several ways.

2 I had a hard time deciding which cartoons to include and how to arrange them. Should I try to put all of my cartoons up, or only the very best ones? It took weeks just to plan out the site content.

3 Next, I had to learn HTML. Web designers use it to specify little details, like type size, and major things, like how the pages on a site are organized. HTML, or HyperText Markup Language, is a computer programming language. I had so much to learn. I didn't even know how to make a link!

4 I had to accept that some of my design ideas didn't look so great on screen. I thought it would be cool to have a black background with purple type. It was almost impossible to read. I had to redo some pages over and over to get them right.

5 Now I think of my site as a work in progress. It's not perfect, but as I learn more about Web design, it's getting better and better. If I keep working at it, I know someday it will look just the way I want it to.

What's the topic?

_____

What organizational structure does the writer use? Refer to pages 124–127 of the *Good Writer's Guide* if you need help.

_____

_____

Is there a clear transition between paragraphs 1 and 2? Revise the first sentence in paragraph 2 to improve the flow of ideas:

_____

_____

_____

_____

_____

Which sentence in paragraph 3 would you move to improve its organization? Use edit marks to show where you would move it.

Rewrite paragraph 4 by adding transitions that improve the flow of ideas:

_____

_____

_____

_____

_____

_____

Writing Rubric

Organization

	Does the writing have a clear structure and is it appropriate for the writer's purpose?	How smoothly do the ideas flow together?
4 Wow!	The writing has a clear structure that is appropriate for the writer's purpose.	The ideas progress in a smooth and orderly way. • The **ideas** flow well from **paragraph** to **paragraph**. • The ideas in each paragraph flow well from one **sentence** to the next. • Meaningful and effective **transitions** connect ideas.
3 Aaah.	The writing has a structure that is <u>generally</u> clear and appropriate for the writer's purpose.	<u>Most</u> of the ideas progress in a smooth and orderly way. • Most of the **ideas** flow well from **paragraph** to **paragraph**. • Most of the ideas in each paragraph flow well from one **sentence** to the next. • Meaningful and effective **transitions** connect most of the ideas.
2 Hmm.	The structure of the writing is not clear or not appropriate for the writer's purpose.	<u>Some</u> of the ideas progress in a smooth and orderly way. • Some of the **ideas** flow well from **paragraph** to **paragraph**. • Some of the ideas in each paragraph flow well from one **sentence** to the next. • Meaningful and effective **transitions** connect some of the ideas.
1 Huh?	The writing does not have a structure.	<u>Few or none</u> of the ideas progress in a smooth and orderly way. The ideas in the paragraphs and sentences do not flow well together and are not connected with transitions.

Organize Your Paragraphs

Choose a paragraph topic from the box. Plan the main idea and details.

Paragraph Topics

- writing in a blog or journal
- downloading music from the Internet
- using a digital camera
- your favorite musician or band
- your favorite Web site
- sharing photographs online

Topic: _____

Main Idea: _____

Details: _____

Write your paragraph. State the main idea in a topic sentence at the <u>beginning</u>.

_____
_____
_____
_____
_____
_____
_____
_____
_____
_____
_____
_____

Choose another paragraph topic from page 41. Plan the main idea and details.

Topic: _____ Details: _____

_____ _____

Main Idea: _____ _____

_____ _____

_____ _____

_____ _____

Write your paragraph. State the main idea in a topic sentence at the <u>end</u>.

_____

_____

_____

_____

_____

_____

_____

_____

_____

_____

_____

_____

_____

_____

_____

_____

_____

_____

_____

_____

Organize Your Paragraphs, continued

Choose one more paragraph topic from page 41. Plan the main idea and details.

Topic: _____

Main Idea: _____

_____

_____

_____

_____

Details: _____

_____

_____

_____

_____

_____

_____

Write your paragraph. Create a different effect by placing the topic sentence in the <u>middle</u>.

_____

_____

_____

_____

_____

_____

_____

_____

_____

_____

_____

_____

_____

_____

_____

_____

_____

_____

Logical Order in Paragraphs

Paragraph Topics	Logical Organizations
• different types of Web sites • your favorite writers or books • an influential musical artist • how teenagers can share their writing, artwork, or knowledge	• from general to specific • from specific to general • from least important to most important • from most important to least important

**Choose a topic and a logical organization from the box.
Plan and then write a paragraph about your topic.**

Topic: _____

Organization: _____

```
┌─────────────────────────────────────────────┐
│                                             │
└─────────────────────────────────────────────┘
                      ↓
┌─────────────────────────────────────────────┐
│                                             │
└─────────────────────────────────────────────┘
                      ↓
┌─────────────────────────────────────────────┐
│                                             │
└─────────────────────────────────────────────┘
```

_____

_____

_____

_____

_____

_____

_____

_____

_____

_____

_____

Chronological Order in Paragraphs

Complete the sentence to brainstorm ideas for writing a paragraph using chronological order.

A funny series of things happened the last time I: _____

_____

_____

Use the flowchart to list the events in chronological order. Then write your paragraph.

First Event

Event 2

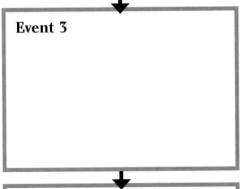

Event 3

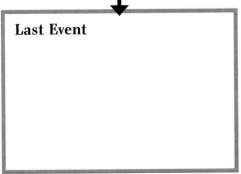

Last Event

Cause and Effect in Paragraphs

Read the paragraph.

> As a photographer for the school newspaper, Bryan was responsible for taking pictures at school athletic events. But today, photography was the last thing on his mind. In fact, he almost forgot all about the football game that afternoon.

How could you revise the paragraph to show cause-and-effect relationships?
Use the graphic organizer for planning. Then rewrite the paragraph.

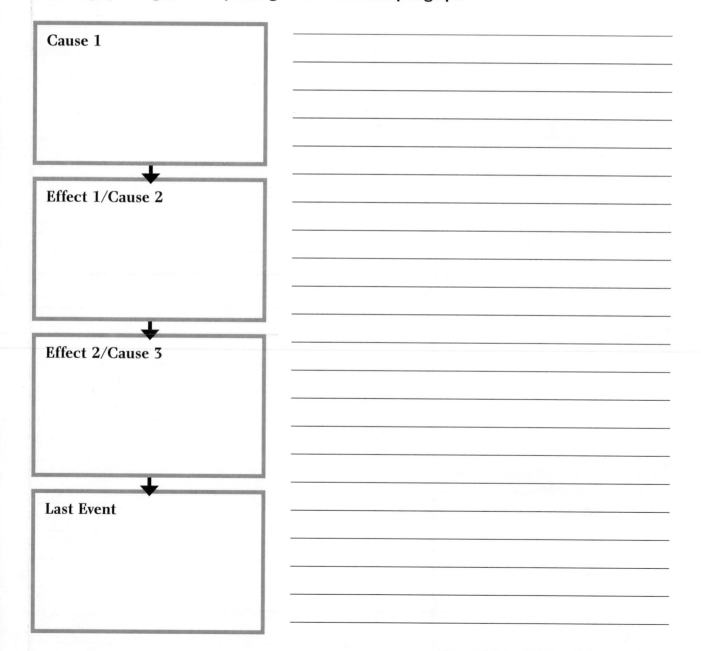

Cause 1

Effect 1/Cause 2

Effect 2/Cause 3

Last Event

Spatial Order in Paragraphs

Plan a paragraph by labeling the different parts of the picture.

Day and Night, 1938, M.C. Escher.

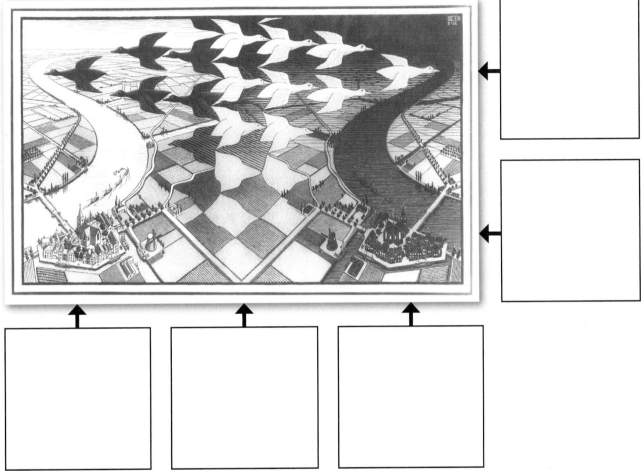

Use spatial order to write a paragraph that describes the picture.

Comparison and Contrast in Paragraphs

Choose a paragraph topic from the box.

Paragraph Topics

- song lyrics and poetry
- painting and photography
- dancing and playing a sport
- a book and the film version of the book

Fill in the T-chart to plan a paragraph that compares or contrasts the two things.

Now write your paragraph.

_____

_____

_____

_____

_____

_____

_____

_____

_____

_____

_____

_____

_____

Problem and Solution in Paragraphs

Choose a paragraph topic from the box or think of your own topic.

Paragraph Topics

- Maria wants to try out for the school play, but she suffers from stage fright.
- Matt's band is supposed to play at the Battle of the Bands tonight, but his drummer just quit.
- Marisa wants to join the school newspaper and the Art Club, but they meet on the same day each week.

Use the graphic organizer below to plan a problem-and-solution paragraph.

Problem:

Solutions:

Now write your paragraph.

_____

_____

_____

_____

_____

_____

_____

_____

_____

_____

_____

Opinions and Support in Paragraphs

Read the opinion statements. Check whether you agree or disagree.

Opinion Statements	Agree	Disagree
1. Today anyone can become famous, even people who have no talent.		
2. Most popular music sounds the same. Truly original artists rarely make it onto the airwaves.		
3. Everyone needs some form of creative expression, whether it's writing, dancing, painting, or even just dressing in your own unique style.		

Choose one opinion statement from the list or think of one of your own. Use the graphic organizer to plan a paragraph that states your opinion and supports it with arguments. Then write your paragraph.

Opinion
Supporting Arguments

_____
_____
_____
_____
_____
_____
_____
_____
_____
_____
_____
_____
_____
_____
_____
_____
_____
_____
_____
_____
_____
_____

Getting Your Paragraph to Flow

Use the information in the T-chart to write a paragraph. Use transition words and phrases to connect ideas and guide your reader.

MP3 Players	CDs
one song=3 megabytes (MB) of space	one song=32 megabytes (MB) of space
takes minutes to download song	takes as long as an hour or more to download song
okay sound quality	good sound quality
all-in-one, small, portable device	large portable device that requires a CD

Now write your paragraph.

_____

_____

_____

_____

_____

_____

_____

_____

_____

_____

_____

_____

_____

_____

_____

_____

_____

_____

_____

_____

Getting Your Paragraph to Flow, continued

Now choose a topic of your own. Organize your thinking with a graphic organizer that works well for the points you want to cover. (See pages 30–37 in the *Good Writer's Guide* for some possibilities.)

Now write your paragraph. Use transition words and phrases to connect ideas and guide your reader.

_____

_____

_____

_____

_____

_____

_____

_____

_____

_____

_____

_____

_____

_____

_____

_____

Organizing an Essay: Prewriting

Use pages 53–56 to plan, draft, and revise an essay. Choose an essay topic from the box or write about a topic of your own.

Essay Topics

- an artist, actor, or writer whom you admire
- a time that you performed in front of a group
- a creative project that you would like to do
- a musical instrument you play (or would like to learn)

Use the space below to organize your paragraphs and plan the flow of your ideas.

Topic: _____

Organizing an Essay: First Draft

Use your plan from page 53 to write the first draft of your essay on pages 54–55.

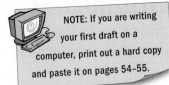

NOTE: If you are writing your first draft on a computer, print out a hard copy and paste it on pages 54–55.

Drafting Checklist for Organization

❑ Your central idea is clearly stated in the first paragraph.

❑ You have followed your graphic organizer to arrange your paragraphs in an effective order.

❑ The details within each paragraph are organized logically.

❑ You have used transitions to help guide the reader.

Organizing an Essay: First Draft, continued

Organizing Your Essay: Revising

Use the questions below to help you revise your first draft on pages 54–55.

1. Can your central idea be more clearly stated in the first paragraph? How can you improve it?

_____

_____

_____

2. Are your paragraphs in the most effective order? Write your main ideas in sticky notes and move them around to see if you can find a more effective order.

3. How can you use transitions between and within paragraphs to better connect your ideas? The chart below lists some transition words and phrases.

Some Transition Words and Phrases			
also	during	in fact	therefore
although	finally	similarly	to begin with
because	however	since	yet

4. What other changes can you make to improve your essay?

_____

_____

_____

_____

_____

Now mark all your changes on pages 54–55.

Development of Ideas

Score the essay using the Writing Rubric on page 58. Then answer the questions.

Score	1	2	3	4

Experience Matters

1   I didn't think finding a summer job would be hard. When I started looking for various jobs around my neighborhood, I realized that it wasn't that easy.

2   I tried looking through the classified ads in the Sunday newspaper. Every job listing seemed to include the phrase "experience necessary." Unfortunately, I'd never held a "real" job before.

3   However, I realized I did have some useful skills to offer employers. For example, I'd been in charge of the decorations committee for the Junior Prom. First, I had to schedule meetings and figure out what tasks we needed to accomplish. I also had to handle the conflicts between students who disagreed about what our prom theme should be. Finally, when it came time to decorate the gym, I scheduled people to do the work. Some of my softball-team buddies tried to shirk their duties, but I made sure everyone did his or her part—including my friends. I learned a lot about managing a group.

4   After looking back on that experience, I decided to apply for a job as an assistant coach for the local girls' softball league.

What's the central idea of the essay?

_____

_____

Write a more interesting beginning for the essay.

_____

_____

_____

_____

_____

_____

Underline good details the writer uses to develop ideas in paragraph 3.

Rewrite the conclusion to do a better job of wrapping up the important details.

_____

_____

_____

_____

_____

_____

Writing Rubric

Development of Ideas

	How thoughtful and interesting is the writing?	How well are the ideas explained and supported?
4 Wow!	The writing engages the reader with worthwhile ideas and an interesting presentation.	The ideas are fully explained and supported. • The ideas are well developed with important details and examples. • The writing feels complete, and the reader is satisfied.
3 Aaah.	<u>Most</u> of the writing engages the reader with worthwhile ideas and an interesting presentation.	<u>Most</u> of the ideas are explained and supported. • Most of the ideas are developed with important details and examples. • The writing feels mostly complete, but the reader is left with some questions.
2 Hmm.	<u>Some</u> of the writing engages the reader with worthwhile ideas and an interesting presentation.	<u>Some</u> of the ideas are explained and supported. • Only some of the ideas are developed. Details and examples are limited. • The writing leaves the reader with many questions.
1 Huh?	The writing does <u>not</u> engage the reader.	The ideas are <u>not</u> explained or supported. The ideas lack details and examples, and the writing feels incomplete.

Engage the Reader from the Start

Read each paragraph. Write some new beginning sentences for the paragraph that will do a better job of engaging the reader.

Ways to Engage the Reader

- thought-provoking question or statistic
- interesting quotation
- unusual metaphor or analogy
- experience familiar to the reader

Volunteering with Animals

Volunteering at an animal shelter is a good way to prepare for a career as a veterinarian. Working in a shelter can provide valuable experience with animals that are ill or injured. You can give the animals attention and affection that they might not have otherwise. Volunteers walk the dogs and help clean and groom cats, dogs, and other animals. Working in a shelter is a great way to learn more about animal care.

---

1. Mahatma Gandhi said, "The greatness of a nation and its moral progress can be judged by the way its animals are treated."

2. _____

3. _____

4. _____

A Major Decision

    <u>Some college students decide on a major right away, but</u> <u>those students are rare.</u> Most first-year students spend the first semester or two exploring their options. Students might choose a traditional major, such as psychology or physics, or a newer field, such as genetics or urban studies. And, of course, there are majors designed to prepare students for further schooling, such as pre-medicine and pre-law. Many students change majors a few times before graduation.

---

5. _____

_____

_____

_____

6. _____

_____

_____

_____

7. _____

_____

_____

_____

8. _____

_____

_____

_____

Develop Ideas in Nonfiction

Read the skimpy nonfiction paragraph. Then use some of the "Ways to Elaborate in Nonfiction" to expand upon the ideas presented. (You may have to do some research to find relevant data to include in charts or tables.)

Ways to Elaborate in Nonfiction

- Add specific examples.
- Add details and explanations.
- Add visuals, such as graphs, tables, and photographs.

1.

Many people think that American teenagers just go to school, have extracurricular activities, and hang out with their friends. Many teenagers also have part-time jobs. Some typical jobs for teenagers include working in restaurants, babysitting, and working as sales clerks in stores. These are often minimum-wage jobs.

_____

_____

_____

_____

_____

_____

_____

_____

_____

_____

_____

_____

_____

_____

_____

_____

2.

Turning 16 usually brings a legal right to the car keys. The dramatic increase in the number of teen driver accidents has caused many concerned parents and lawmakers to examine teen driver issues. Motor vehicle accidents are the leading cause of death for 15- to 20-year-olds. As a result, many states are creating new laws to reduce teen driver accidents.

_____
_____
_____
_____
_____
_____
_____
_____
_____
_____
_____
_____
_____
_____
_____
_____
_____
_____
_____

Develop Ideas in Fiction

Look at each photograph and read the bare-bones story beside it. Then use the "Ways to Elaborate in Fiction" to enrich the story.

Ways to Elaborate in Fiction

- Add dialogue between characters.
- Add sensory details. What should the reader see, hear, and feel?

1.

Jared was running as fast as he could. He was tired. He didn't know if he was going to make it to the audition in time. He had a particularly rough morning. He was determined to make a good impression. He had one thing on his mind: playing the lead role in the school play.

_____

_____

_____

_____

_____

_____

_____

_____

_____

_____

_____

_____

_____

_____

_____

_____

_____

2.

Kristen was angry. She had played a good game, but she was being challenged. She felt exhausted. She had injured her knee and her ego at the same time. She felt like there was no one on her side. She was about to quit the team.

_____

_____

_____

_____

_____

_____

_____

_____

_____

_____

_____

_____

_____

_____

_____

_____

_____

_____

_____

Build Strong Conclusions

Read the essay. Rewrite the conclusion in two different ways to make it more effective.

Strong Ways to Conclude an Essay

- relate ideas to the thesis statement
- summarize major points
- pose or answer a question
- quote a memorable line
- cite a dramatic or personal example

Become a Tutor

Are you good with equations? A whiz at Spanish or French? How are your computer skills? If you excel in a certain subject area, you should consider a job as a tutor. Not only can you make decent money, you can also improve your own understanding of a subject as you explain it to someone else.

Working as a tutor looks impressive on a résumé as well. When you apply for a job, employers will see that you have experience teaching an important subject. Tutoring also helps develop your communication skills. Employers value these, so a tutoring background might put you ahead of other job applicants.

Many people become tutors. It is good to help others.

Conclusion 1. _____

_____

_____

_____

_____

Conclusion 2. _____

_____

_____

_____

_____

Read the essay and rewrite the conclusion in two different ways. Use techniques different from the ones you used on page 65.

Behind the Scenes

When our school puts on a play, naturally the audience focuses on the actors. They're the ones up on stage under the hot lights, covered in heavy greasepaint, hoping they don't forget their lines. But the people working backstage are equally important. If you've ever helped to put on a play, you know how much work goes on behind the scenes.

For example, the director provides guidance to the actors. Other crew members handle costumes and makeup. And let's not forget the students in charge of the set design and props. All of us work together to capture the audience's imagination.

<u>Personally, I really love being involved in designing sets for our school plays.</u>

Conclusion 1. _____

_____

_____

_____

_____

_____

_____

Conclusion 2. _____

_____

_____

_____

_____

_____

_____

Voice and Style

Score the essay using the Writing Rubric on page 68. Then answer the questions.

Score	1	2	3	4

A Misunderstanding

1   Last week, I saw what happens when two people do not tell each other everything. It all started when I saw a poster telling people to run for student government. I remembered my friend Ryan telling me a few weeks ago that he might like to run for something. I heard there were going to be elections held for student council. I decided to nominate him for class treasurer. I wrote his name on a piece of paper and slipped it into the nomination box in the lunch room.

2   The candidates' names were announced during homeroom the next morning. Ryan's name was one of them. He looked surprised but not happy. We sat down at the lunch table later on. He looked kind of mad. I told him I had nominated him for treasurer. I also told him I thought he would be good at the job. Everyone knows he's good at math.

3   It turns out he had changed his mind about getting involved. Apparently, he decided not to run when his older brother told him he would have to deliver a speech in front of the class. Ryan does not feel comfortable with public speaking. He ended up removing his name from the ballot. Meanwhile, I learned not to make assumptions about my friends.

Which sentences in paragraph 1 could be more powerful and engaging? Revise them.

_____

_____

_____

_____

_____

Which words are repeated too often? Delete them. Then rewrite paragraph 2 to introduce more sentence variety.

_____

_____

_____

_____

_____

Rewrite paragraph 3 to make the tone more informal, to go with the personal topic.

_____

_____

_____

_____

_____

_____

_____

_____

Writing Rubric

	Voice and Style	
	Does the writing sound real and is it unique to the writer?	**Are the words and sentences interesting and appropriate to the purpose and audience?**
4 Wow!	The writing fully engages the reader with its individual voice and style. The tone is consistent throughout.	The words and sentences are interesting and appropriate to the purpose and audience. • The words are powerful and engaging. • The sentences are varied and flow together effectively.
3 Aaah.	Most of the writing engages the reader with a voice and style that are unique. The tone is mostly consistent.	Most of the words and sentences are interesting and appropriate to the purpose and audience. • Most words are powerful and engaging. • Most sentences are varied and flow together.
2 Hmm.	Some of the writing engages the reader, but the voice and style are not unique.	Some of the words and sentences are interesting and appropriate to the purpose and audience. • Some words are powerful and engaging. • Some sentences are varied, but the flow could be smoother.
1 Huh?	The writing does not engage the reader.	Few or none of the words and sentences are appropriate to the purpose and audience. • The words are often vague and dull. • The sentences lack variety and do not flow together.

Choosing the Right Voice

Describe the photograph, adapting your voice to go with the purpose and audience.

1. Write to inform your friends.

_____

_____

_____

_____

2. Write to entertain a 7-year-old.

_____

_____

_____

_____

3. Write to persuade a teacher.

_____

_____

_____

_____

Describe the photograph, adapting your voice to go with the purpose and audience.

4. Write to amuse your classmates.

_____

_____

_____

_____

5. Write to explain the photograph to your family.

_____

_____

_____

_____

6. Write to hold a class of first-graders in suspense.

_____

_____

_____

_____

Choosing Effective Words

Edit the paragraph. Replace each underlined word with a more precise or vivid word from the chart.

Nouns	Verbs	Adjectives	Adverbs
words	portrays	old-time	incorrectly
dialogue	spoken	washed-up	wrongly
stars	uttered	classic	imprecisely
moviegoers	delivered	accurate	inaccurately
pianist	announced	memorable	

Misquoted Movies

If you like ~~old~~ *classic* movies, you probably know a lot of <u>great</u> lines like, "Play it

again, Sam" from *Casablanca* (1942). However, the <u>lines</u> you remember may not

be exactly <u>right</u>. For example, the words "Play it again, Sam" were not <u>said</u> by

either of the <u>lead actors</u> in *Casablanca*, Humphrey Bogart and Ingrid Bergman.

Instead, Bogart tells a nightclub <u>musician</u>, "You played it for her, you can play

it for me.... If she can stand it, I can. Play it!" Many people also remember

the ending of *Sunset Boulevard* (1950) <u>wrongly</u>. In this <u>well-known</u> film, Gloria

Swanson <u>plays</u> a former star named Norma Desmond. Many people think her

last line is "I'm ready for my closeup, Mr. DeMille." In fact, it's "All right, Mr.

DeMille, I'm ready for my closeup."

Edit the paragraphs. Replace dull or ineffective words with more precise or vivid ones. Add modifiers, too.

What's My Line?

Movies aren't the only sources of misquotation. People also get other things wrong. For instance, many people think they're quoting Sherlock Holmes when they say, "Elementary, my dear Watson." But Holmes never says this to his friend in any of the Sherlock Holmes books. Likewise, people believe that Tarzan meets Jane in the forest and says "Me Tarzan, you Jane." This line appears nowhere in Edgar Rice Burroughs's first Tarzan book, *Tarzan of the Apes*, nor is it used in the rest of the Tarzan books or the movies that came later.

Quotes from people in history may also not be real. For example, there's nothing to support the belief that Paul Revere went though the streets crying, "The British are coming!" in 1776. It would have been strange if he had, since most people living in the American colonies still thought of *themselves* as British subjects. Around the same time in history, French ruler Marie Antoinette is supposed to have said, "Let them eat cake!" when she heard that the poor people of France had no bread. There's no proof of her having really said this. People writing about her now think this quote may have come from an earlier ruler.

Add Color to Your Language: Similes

A simile compares two unlike things using the words *like* or *as*.
Write your interpretation of each simile.

1. Taneisha's smile is as bright as a flashing neon sign.

_____

_____

2. Aaron thinks he's so funny, but his sense of humor is like a dull, rusty blade.

_____

_____

3. I was so tired, the words on the page swarmed together like a colony of tiny black ants.

_____

_____

4. Falling in love is like feeling the sun warming your back—and then realizing you forgot to put on sunscreen.

_____

_____

5. Layla's arguments were as clear as mud.

_____

_____

Now create three similes of your own and explain what each one means.

6. Simile: _____

Meaning: _____

_____

7. Simile: _____

Meaning: _____

_____

8. Simile: _____

Meaning: _____

_____

Add Color to Your Language: Metaphors

A metaphor compares two unlike things by saying one thing *is* the other thing. Write your interpretation of each metaphor.

1. History is a scarcely legible letter with half the lines blacked out.

_____

_____

2. In the end, this movie is a bowl of stale popcorn with fake butter flavor.

_____

_____

3. His voice was a pointy little red pen circling everything that had gone wrong.

_____

_____

4. The starlet's ego was a big fat balloon, and that review was the pin that popped it.

_____

_____

5. Robert is a sheep, just following everyone else.

_____

_____

Now create three metaphors of your own and explain what each one means.

6. Metaphor: _____

Meaning: _____

_____

7. Metaphor: _____

Meaning: _____

_____

8. Metaphor: _____

Meaning: _____

_____

Add Color to Your Language: Idioms

An idiom is a familiar expression that's not literally true.
Explain the meaning of each underlined idiom.

1. I agreed to go out with Jane because, as my father always said, <u>you shouldn't judge a book by its cover</u>.

_____

_____

2. When Jane and I started dating, I was <u>on cloud nine</u> at first, but she quickly lost interest in me.

_____

_____

3. "Looks like I <u>dropped the ball</u> again," Jane said, calling at the last minute to cancel our date.

_____

_____

4. "This is the third date she's missed!" my friend Nate scolded. "<u>Do the math</u>, dude. This relationship isn't worth the aggravation!"

_____

_____

5. That night, my buddies and I went to the movies and had a great time—<u>just what the doctor ordered</u>.

_____

_____

Write two idioms you frequently use and explain what each one means.

6. Idiom: _____

Meaning: _____

_____

_____

7. Idiom: _____

Meaning: _____

_____

_____

Add Color to Your Language:
Pull It All Together

Use pages 76–78 to describe a typical day in your life. Use similes, metaphors, and idioms to make your description more colorful.

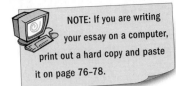
NOTE: If you are writing your essay on a computer, print out a hard copy and paste it on page 76–78.

Add Color to Your Language, continued

78

Stay Active!

Edit the passage. Change sentences written in the passive voice to the active voice.

Three Modern-Day Princesses

They were called "the Buffys" by everyone at Tropical High School, though Buffy was actually the name of just one of them. Buffy was envied by all of her peers. She had lips as pink as a wad of bubblegum, eyes as blue as chlorinated pool water, and hair as golden as the costly jewelry her dad regularly bought for her. (She was believed by her classmates to be the richest girl in town.) Of course, her outfits always looked perfect. Her hair was styled by the most expensive, exclusive hairdressers. And her deep tan was marveled at by everyone who met her. It never went away, even in the middle of winter.

Tara and Tracy were considered by Buffy to be her very best friends. After all, they were the three most attractive, popular girls at school, so naturally they stuck together. Of course, when guys were around, too much attention was paid to Buffy. But Tara and Tracy had long since resigned themselves to that.

Were the three girls actually royalty? No. They just acted like they were.

Avoiding Repetition

Edit the passage to remove or replace the repeated words and phrases.

The Buffys and the Beast

Buffy, Tara, and Tracy sat in the back of trigonometry class, having their own private conversation as usual. As usual, their conversation focused on boys. They loved to talk about boys. One boy in particular fascinated them. No one had seen him for nearly a year. That boy was 17-year-old surfer Brandon Bailey. He hadn't been seen at school since his mysterious surfing accident a year ago.

"I totally drive past Brandon's house at least twice a week," Tara said.

"Why do you keep driving past Brandon's house?" Tracy asked Tara with a questioning look. Tara answered Tracy saying that she just hopes to catch a glimpse of him.

At that point, Buffy broke into the conversation, speaking up and saying, "I keep hoping for the same thing! I've heard people tell all sorts of stories, but I wonder what the truth really is."

Buffy, Tara, and Tracy sat and discussed the Brandon mystery for a while longer. They did not know the truth. The truth was far worse than anyone could have guessed. The truth was that the stress of the accident had made his hormones go crazy. Hormones affect hair growth. Brandon's hair had started growing like wild! Brandon had become all furry, and he was ashamed to go out in public.

Varying Your Sentences: Beginnings and Types

Edit the passage for sentence variety. Use different sentence beginnings and different sentence types.

The Baileys' House

"Well, Brandon may be ugly, but I bet his house is still nice," Tara remarked wistfully. "It's too bad we can never find out for sure now," she added sadly.

Buffy and Tracy nodded knowingly. People had only heard rumors about the Bailey family's fabulous beach house. Buffy and her class thought it was the coolest house in town. Buffy and her friends had never actually been inside. Still, they knew that the house had every luxury.

According to the rumors, the Baileys could afford the local cable company's mega-deluxe plan. According to some people, guests could choose from over 500 channels of action-packed entertainment. Plus, there was an enormous swimming pool in the backyard. Supposedly, there were also coconut and mango trees growing in the yard.

The girls longed to see the house's interior, but they knew they never would. Brandon had shut himself up inside, and the Baileys no longer invited people to visit. The house was closed to them, and that was that.

Varying Your Sentences: Length

Edit the passage. Make some sentences long and some short.

Buffy's Stepmother Spoils the Weekend

Thinking about Brandon made Buffy sad. But she didn't stay sad for long. Tara was throwing a party that weekend. Buffy was really looking forward to it.

Unfortunately, Buffy's stepmother had other ideas. She was very concerned about Buffy's grades. Buffy was failing trigonometry and barely passing French. If her grades didn't improve, she might not graduate.

That Friday, Buffy headed home after school. Her stepmother met her at the door. "How's French class going?" she asked coldly.

"It's going OK, I guess," Buffy mumbled. She couldn't look her stepmother in the eye. "I've got a test coming up on Monday." Immediately, Buffy regretted opening her mouth. Her stepmother was smiling at her triumphantly.

"I guess you need to study, then," she said. "Looks like you'll be spending the weekend at your desk."

Buffy could not believe her ears. "You've got to be kidding!" she exclaimed. "No way can I miss Tara's party!"

"No more socializing until your grades improve, and that's final."

Join Neighboring Sentences

Edit the passage. Use *and*, *but*, or *or* to join neighboring sentences.

A Defiant Damsel in Distress

Buffy didn't exactly have permission to go to Tara's party. She was going anyway. After all, she had actually studied that morning. She deserved a break.

Buffy knew her stepmother didn't like spending weekends at home any more than Buffy herself did. Her stepmother often went to the beauty salon on Saturday afternoons. Sometimes, she went shopping. Buffy waited quietly in her room. She pretended she was working. She couldn't wait for her stepmother to leave.

As soon as the coast was clear, Buffy slipped out the front door. She wondered which route she should take. Should she walk down the main road? Should she sneak through her neighbors' yards? The main road was quicker. The yards were the best way to avoid being seen.

Unfortunately, the houses and yards and trees all looked alike. Buffy was soon lost. She gazed around the yard she was in, looking for a landmark. A coconut fell from a tree above. It hit her on the head. She was knocked out.

Needless to say, when the Baileys arrived home, they were a bit surprised.

Join Sentences with Related Ideas

Edit the passage. Use connecting words to join sentences with related ideas.

Connecting Words		
Time	**Cause-and-Effect**	**Other Relationships**
when as soon as	because since	although unless
after while	so as a result	even though however

The Princess Is Rescued

The Baileys brought Buffy inside. She had woken up. She had been unconscious for hours under the hot sun. Her skin was pink from sunburn. Her head ached. She was eager to speak to the family that had helped her. "I'm Buffy," she said weakly.

"Well, Buffy, I think you should stay here and rest until you feel better," said a gentle female voice. Buffy looked up into the kind face of a woman about her parents' age. Out of the corner of her eye, she saw a teenage boy and his older sister stood nearby.

"Thanks, that's very kind," said Buffy. The boy silently fetched another icepack for Buffy's throbbing head. His mom reached for the remote control. "Let's see if there's anything good for you kids to watch," she said.

Buffy was disappointed that her rescuers didn't subscribe to the premium cable channels. She didn't mention her disappointment. All afternoon and evening, the teens hung out together watching old sitcoms. Buffy decided to stay for a while. This family was so much nicer than her own.

Move the Details!

Combine the sentences by moving details from one sentence to another or by adding appositives.

1.
| Buffy wished she could stay with this lovely family forever. Buffy was the most popular girl in school. | _____
_____
_____
_____ |

2.
| That afternoon, Buffy awoke from a nap. The house seemed quiet. | _____
_____
_____ |

3.
| She could hear faint noises. They were coming from the yard. | _____
_____
_____
_____ |

4.
| The Baileys were all planting their garden. The Baileys were a large family. | _____
_____
_____
_____ |

5.
| Brandon rolled up his sleeves and showed his forearms. His forearms were covered in fur. | _____
_____
_____
_____ |

Use *Who*, *Whose*, *Which*, and *That*

Use *who*, *whose*, *which*, or *that* to combine sentences that tell about the same person or thing.

1.

Buffy ran back into the house and threw herself on the couch. Now she was sobbing.	_____ _____ _____ _____

2.

Brandon's sister came inside. Her name was Beth.	_____ _____ _____ _____

3.

She decided to tell Buffy the truth. Her brother was not what he seemed.	_____ _____ _____ _____

4.

Buffy listened as Beth described Brandon's furry issue. It sounded like a permanent condition.	_____ _____ _____ _____

5.

Buffy pondered her situation. The situation felt like a bad dream.	_____ _____ _____ _____

Condense Ideas and Details

Combine sentences to use fewer, more precise words.

1.

| Buffy went out to the backyard. It was the smallest backyard in town. Brandon shoveled dirt in the garden. Brandon was careful not to get dirt on Buffy. | _____ _____ _____ _____ _____ |

2.

| Brandon gazed down at the earth that he had just turned. He looked anxious. Buffy held Brandon's hand in hers. It was the hairiest hand she'd ever seen. | _____ _____ _____ _____ _____ |

Use a verb's –ed form as a modifier and combine the sentences.

3.

| Brandon suddenly blurted out an invitation to the prom. The invitation caught Buffy by surprise. | _____ _____ _____ _____ |

Use a verb's –ing form as a modifier and combine the sentences.

4.

| Then Buffy frowned. She suddenly became worried about what her shallow friends would think. | _____ _____ _____ _____ |

Read the passage. Then edit the passage to combine sentences using any of the techniques you've learned.

Techniques for Combining Sentences

1. Join neighboring sentences.

2. Join related ideas.

3. Move details from one sentence to another.

4. Use *who, whose, which,* and *that.*

5. Condense ideas and details.

Happily Ever After?

On prom night, Buffy's friends huddled in the corner. They were gossiping about her. They were quietly talking about her all night. She tried to ignore her friends' awkward looks. She and Brandon danced together. They danced all night. As they danced, they talked about their plans for the future.

"I'm thinking of opening my own beauty salon some day," Buffy revealed. "You know, where people could come and get their hair styled." She paused. "Or they could get hair-removal treatments if they need it. In fact—"

Brandon looked offended. He interrupted her. "Are you sure you have the math skills for this, Buffy?" he asked. "Can you really run your own business?"

Buffy looked down at her perfectly polished toenails. She didn't answer. Brandon would learn that there was more to her than a pretty face. She also had great hair, perfect skin, and a dream of owning her own business.

Brandon pulled her closer. "My mom's a whiz with numbers, and she can lend you some money to get your business started."

Buffy pondered what Brandon had said. Buffy's mind wandered deeper into the issue. She wondered why Brandon's family only had the basic cable plan. She knew they could definitely afford a better plan. She thought about why they had never upgraded to a better cable plan.

Written Conventions

**Score the essay using the Writing Rubric on page 90.
Then edit the essay to fix:**

Score	1	2	3	4

- incomplete sentences
- incorrect punctuation
- misspelled and misused words

Practicing Patience

When I walked into karate class. I was surrounded by a sea of mirrors and multi-colored floor mats. All I could think about was my own awkwardness. As I walked across the wooden floor of the dojo. Suddenly I felt totally self-conscience.

However I soon realized everyone else felt just as wierd as I did. Who wouldn't feel awkward standing around barefoot in an outfit that looked like lose white pajamas? My friend Luis caught my eye and loudly whispered, Is my belt tied correctly? We waited nervously for the teacher to arrive.

Once class started we didn't stay nervous for long. Our teacher immedietely got us moving. We had to stretch our muscles. Before we learned any moves. I straitened my leg out. Then I struggled to bend my head down to my knee I couldn't quiet do it.

By the end of the class my muscles were soar. Our teacher was real encouraging though. Trust me, he said, with a little patience your going to become karate master's.

Written Conventions

	Are the sentences written correctly?	Does the writing show correct punctuation, capitalization, and spelling?
4 Wow!	The sentences are complete and correct. Fragments may be used on purpose to achieve an effect.	The writing is free of major errors in punctuation, capitalization, and spelling.
3 Aaah.	<u>Most</u> of the sentences are complete and correct.	The writing has <u>some</u> errors in punctuation, capitalization, and spelling.
2 Hmm.	<u>Few</u> of the sentences are complete and correct, but the reader can understand the meaning.	The writing has <u>many</u> errors in punctuation, capitalization, and spelling.
1 Huh?	The sentences are <u>not</u> complete and correct. The writing is difficult to read and understand.	The errors in punctuation, capitalization, and spelling make the writing difficult to read and understand.

Use Modifiers Carefully

Edit the text to make the meaning clear. Add, change, or move words as needed.

1.

> Karaoke has been around for about 20 years. Beginning as a popular after-work
>
> activity for Japanese business people, amateur vocalists all over the world now
>
> enjoy karaoke.

2.

> Singing along to popular songs from every era, the karaoke machine is always a big
>
> hit. It appeals to people of all ages.

3.

> First, you choose a song from the machine whose lyrics and melody you know well.
>
> Worried about forgetting a line? Relax. Appearing on the karaoke screen, your
>
> memory will soon be refreshed by the lyrics.

4.

> Afraid of not sounding good, there are nervous moments at first for beginning
>
> karaoke singers.

5.

> Karaoke is less intimidating with a group of friends. Singing with a group, audiences
>
> won't even notice if your voice isn't perfect.

Use the Right Word

Fix the misspelled or misused words in the passage.
Use proofreading and editing marks to show your revisions.

An Island Party

Hosting a party is a lot of work, specially if the party has a theme. The people of the Hawaiin aisles celebrate many special occassions with a party called a luau. For instance, a luau might be thrown when a couple gets marred or when someone gradjuates. The host traditionally puts up a tent in the backyard. The tent is than decorated with flowers. Leis, the traditionally necklaces for guests, can also be made using real or silk flowers.

Another important part of a luau is the music. Many luaus include guitar music or music from a string instrument called a ukullele. However, its a challenge to find a musician who plays the ukulele well, so recordings of Hawaiin music are a poplar second choice.

Of course, food is a vital part of any celebration. Being an island, Hawaii is full of fresh fruit such as mango, papiya, and pineapple. A good spread of fresh fruit looks festive and tastes great on a warm day. Another traditional menu item is barbicued pig, which can be served with sweet potatos. All of these elements will help create a fun atmosfere for you're luau.

Use Correct Punctuation

Use editing marks to correct the punctuation in each exercise.

1. ask ten different people what the word music means and you'll get ten different answers

people have different opinions about music.

2. Of course people can agree on a few basic elements such as melody rhythm beat

and instruments

3. Even these basic terms however can mean different things to different people.

4. A hip-hop beat that's complex fresh and interesting to a teenage audience might seem like

nothing but noise as far as their parents, are concerned.

5. Definitions of music vary across cultures too for example most western music is based on a

seven-note scale (or twelve notes if you include the "half-steps."

6. Music from other parts of the world such as the middle East and the Far East is often

structured around a five-note scale.

Read the passage aloud, using the punctuation marks as "stage directions." (See page 203 of the *Good Writer's Guide*.) Are there any "stage directions" missing or incorrect? Edit the passage, adding or correcting punctuation to make it read properly.

Yoga

Want to get in shape and lower your stress level at the same time. Try attending a yoga class. Yoga developed in India thousands of years ago as a spiritual practice that included exercises and breathing techniques. Most yoga classes in the United States today emphasize the physical postures known as asanas. Some people mistakenly believe that to practice yoga, you need to contort your body in all sorts of uncomfortable ways. So what's the truth. The truth is that many yoga postures are fairly easy even for beginners. You can warm up with poses like the Easy Seated Position— commonly used for meditation—or the mountain pose which involves nothing more than standing up straight and tall. As your muscles grow more limber you can try more challenging poses you should never exert yourself to the point where you feel pain. Yoga instructor Ashanya Mujad says, You can't always tell if you're exerting yourself too much beginners need to be aware of their limits.

Use Complete Sentences

Look for the incomplete sentences in the passage. Then revise the passage, fixing all the incomplete sentences.

A Drum That Speaks

Some instruments are made to mimic the sound of spoken language. One example is the talking drum. An instrument from West Africa. The body of the drum is shaped a little like an hourglass and made of wood. With drum heads at both ends made from animal hides or fish skin tightened around wooden hoops. The talking drum also has leather cords. Stretching from one end to the other. The cords are used to change the pitch of the drum.

When the drummer squeezes the cords. The rising and falling pitch of the drum is used to imitate the sounds of spoken language. Even to sound like the words of well-known sayings and songs.

Talking drums are used to accompany dancers or to send messages. They are often used in festivals and ceremonies. To tell stories. Sounds can travel several miles. Today, the talking drum is popular in many forms of West African music. Talking drums in different sizes are widely used. By the Yoruba people of Ghana.

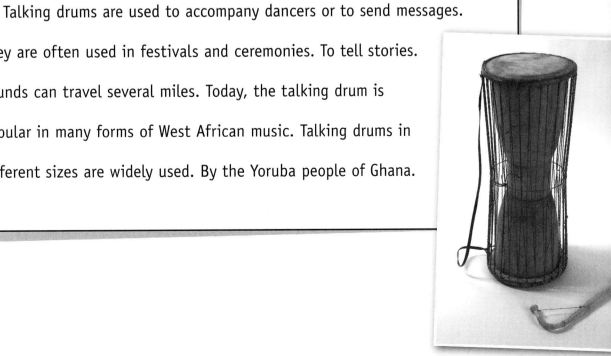

Catch and Correct Mistakes

Identify the Common Error in each sentence. (See pages 208–211 of the *Good Writer's Guide*.) Then rewrite the sentence correctly.

1. Created in the Bronx in the 1970s break dancing is a popular form of expressive dance.

    Common Error: <u>Missing comma after introductory phrase.</u>

    Corrected sentence: _____

    _____

2. Elements of Kung-fu are associated on the movements in break dancing.

    Common Error: _____

    Corrected sentence: _____

    _____

3. Break dancers compete with rival teams, they are dancing to win.

    Common Error: _____

    Corrected sentence: _____

    _____

4. Some forms of dance do not require shoes but break dance should always be done in sneakers.

    Common Error: _____

    Corrected sentence: _____

    _____

5. Being an improvisational form of movement break dancing moves are constantly being added to the mix.

    Common Error: _____

    Corrected sentence: _____

    _____

6. Break dancing may have been influenced by earliness dances such as the Lindy Hop and the Charleston.

    Common Error: _____

    Corrected sentence: _____

    _____

Catch and Correct Mistakes, continued

7. Like breakdancing. Hip-hop music first became widely popular in the 1980s.

Common Error: _____

Corrected sentence: _____

_____

8. Experts believe rappers was influenced by the rhythms of West African storytellers, American blues music, and African American poets.

Common Error: _____

Corrected sentence: _____

_____

9. One early hip-hop artist, a Jamaican teenage immigrant, pioneered the use of two turntables at a time and starts a trend.

Common Error: _____

Corrected sentence: _____

_____

10. When the music video format emerged in the 1980s, they gave rap a larger audience.

Common Error: _____

Corrected sentence: _____

_____

11. Some artists combined hip-hop and rock they chanted new lyrics over classic rock tunes from the 1970s.

Common Error: _____

Corrected sentence: _____

_____

12. Other artists popularized sampling which is the practice of taking snippets from an older recording and incorporating them into a new song.

Common Error: _____

Corrected sentence: _____

_____

Edit the essay to correct all errors in written conventions.

Dance Trends of the Past

Break dancing which became a fad in the 1980's may have had it's roots in dance trends of decades past. In particular the Charleston and the Lindy Hop. These dances, became popular in New York city in the 1920's during the jazz Age. Just as jazz musicians improvise there melodies a dancer felt free to created their own exiting new dance styles.

According to legend the Lindy Hop got it's name from guest in New York's famous Savoy Ballroom. Named "Shorty George" Snowden. One night a reporter ask Snowden what dance the nearby couples was performing. Snowden happen to be looking at a news paper headline that read, "Lindy Hops the Atlantic." (The article was about Charles Lindberghs 1927 flight to Paris France.) Snowden told the reporter, "The Lindy Hop" from then on that's what people call the new dance.

However there is no particularly story behind the name of the Charleston. This dance appeared to have been named for it's place of origin. Experts think the steps were invented by African Americans, who were living on an island near Charleston south Carolina. The Lindy Hop and the Charleston were popular throughout the twenties thirties and forties.

Speak Your Truth

Look at each photograph. Write one truth the photograph speaks to you. Then trade papers with a partner. Compare and discuss your truths.

1.

_____

_____

_____

2.

_____

_____

_____

3.

_____

_____

_____

4.

_____

_____

_____

Explain Your Truth

Choose one of the truths you wrote on page 99. Write a sentence for each box in the idea organizer to explain how you arrived at your truth.

The Story of My Thinking

I used to think . . .	→	But then this happened:	→	So now I think . . .

_____   _____   _____
_____   _____   _____
_____   _____   _____
_____   _____   _____
_____   _____   _____

Now put your sentences together to create a kernel essay.

_____
_____
_____
_____
_____
_____
_____
_____
_____
_____
_____
_____
_____
_____
_____
_____

Explain More Truths

Choose another of the truths you wrote on page 99. Choose a different idea organizer from pages 224–225 in the *Good Writer's Guide* to show how you arrived at your truth.

Now put your sentences together to create a kernel essay.

_____

_____

_____

_____

_____

_____

_____

_____

_____

_____

_____

_____

Explain More Truths, continued

Choose another of the truths you wrote on page 99. Choose a different idea organizer from pages 224–225 in the *Good Writer's Guide* to show how you arrived at your truth.

Now put your sentences together to create a kernel essay.

_____

_____

_____

_____

_____

_____

_____

_____

_____

_____

_____

_____

Ways You Know Things

Look at the skimpy paragraph below. Use the different "Ways You Know Things" to write some details you could add.

Skimpy Writing

The Concert

We went to a concert the other night. It was the best show I have ever seen. The bands played great music. The crowd was very excited.

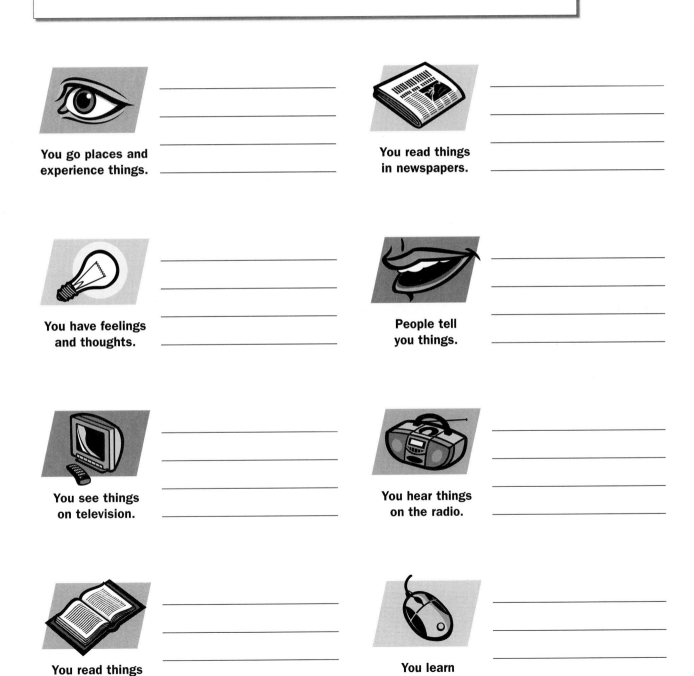

You go places and experience things.

_____
_____
_____
_____

You read things in newspapers.

_____
_____
_____
_____

You have feelings and thoughts.

_____
_____
_____

People tell you things.

_____
_____
_____

You see things on television.

_____
_____
_____

You hear things on the radio.

_____
_____
_____

You read things in books.

_____
_____
_____

You learn things online.

_____
_____
_____

Prove It On Your Own

Use the different "Ways You Know Things" to add details to the skimpy paragraph.

Ways You Know Things

| You go places and experience things. | You have feelings and thoughts. | You see things on television. | You read things in books. | You read things in newspapers. | People tell you things. | You hear things on the radio. | You learn things online. |

Skimpy Writing

The New Roller Coaster

There is a new roller coaster at the amusement park. I think the old roller coaster was better. The new one scores low on the fright scale. I was not impressed with it.

Prove It On Your Own, continued

Use the different "Ways You Know Things" to add details to the skimpy paragraph.

Ways You Know Things

| You go places and experience things. | You have feelings and thoughts. | You see things on television. | You read things in books. | You read things in newspapers. | People tell you things. | You hear things on the radio. | You learn things online. |

Skimpy Writing

Starting the School Day

I think 7:30 in the morning is much too early to start school. Most teenagers don't feel awake and alert at that hour. It's hard to learn anything early in the morning.

_____
_____
_____
_____
_____
_____
_____
_____
_____
_____
_____
_____
_____
_____
_____
_____
_____

Prove It On Your Own, continued

Create a skimpy paragraph in the box below. Make it skimpy on purpose!

Skimpy Writing

_____

_____

_____

_____

_____

Now use different "Ways You Know Things" to develop the ideas with details.

Ba-Da-Bing!

Look at the Ba-Da-Bing plan for developing one of the Memorable Moments.
Then write a developed paragraph incorporating the ideas.

> ### Memorable Moments
> **1.** The weather surprised everyone that day.
> **2.** I was really nervous on my first date.
> **3.** My friend and I had our worst argument ever.
> **4.** Our team played a game to remember.
> **5.** The restaurant we went to was very busy.

Memorable Moment: _The weather surprised everyone that day._

Where You Were

Jack and I were at the World Series during a hailstorm.

What You Saw

People were rushing for cover. Peanut shells were scattered everywhere.

What You Thought

I thought, "I may never see another World Series game in person—so I'm staying!"

_____

_____

_____

_____

_____

_____

_____

© Hampton-Brown

Ba-Da-Bing!, continued

Choose a different moment from the Memorable Moments on page 107.
Plan a Ba-Da-Bing to add details. Then write the developed paragraph.

Memorable Moment: _____

BA	**DA**	**BING**
Where You Were	What You Saw	What You Thought

Take Time for Transitions

Read each story starter. Continue the story using transition words to connect the ideas.

Some Transition Words

afterward	finally	similarly
also	second	since
although	however	therefore
because	in fact	to begin with
earlier	for instance	yet

1.   **An Unlikely Friend**

My friend Tyler and I have the same birthday.
We were both born on October 20, 1989. We met on the first
day of seventh grade. At first, we didn't get along at all. _In fact,_

_____

_____

_____

_____

_____

_____

_____

_____

2.   **Mikey and Me**

When my brother Mikey was born, I wasn't very happy
about it at first. He was so noisy! Also, it seemed that he took
up the whole family's attention all the time. _For instance,_

_____

_____

_____

_____

_____

_____

_____

3.   **Andrea's Wedding**

Last February, I attended my cousin Andrea's wedding in Florida. We were all hoping for the day to be perfect—but, of course, it didn't go exactly as planned. _To begin with,_ _____

_____

_____

_____

_____

_____

_____

_____

_____

4.   Write your own story. Use transitions to connect ideas.

_____

_____

_____

_____

_____

_____

_____

_____

_____

_____

_____

_____

_____

Connect Your Paragraphs

Read the first paragraph of "A Wild Ride." As you write more paragraphs to finish the story, use transitions to connect the paragraphs.

Some Transition Words		
afterward	finally	similarly
also	for instance	since
although	however	therefore
because	in fact	to begin with
earlier	second	yet

A Wild Ride

The day of the big bike ride had finally arrived. I'd been looking forward to it for months. All week, people at school were talking about the new equipment they had bought for the ride. Meanwhile, I was waiting to get my bike back from the repair shop.

Earlier, _____

_____

_____

_____

_____

_____

_____

_____

_____

_____

_____

_____

_____

_____

_____

_____

_____

_____

_____

_____

_____

© Hampton-Brown

Chapter 3 Writing Clinic

Write a story of three or four paragraphs about one of the topics listed, or about another topic of your choice. Use transitions to connect ideas within and between paragraphs.

Story Topics

- a challenge you handled successfully
- the funniest thing that ever happened to you
- a major change in your life

Use the Intensity Scale

Use the Intensity Scale to rewrite the sentences below, replacing vague words with sharp, precise words.

1. VAGUE 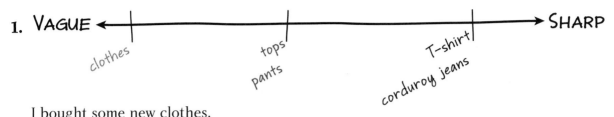 **SHARP**

I bought some new clothes.

I bought a long-sleeved T-shirt and a pair of corduroy jeans.

2. VAGUE  **SHARP**

My trip was fun.

_____

3. VAGUE ← ———————————————— → **SHARP**

Our game was interesting.

_____

4. VAGUE ← ———————————————— → **SHARP**

We visited my relatives and ate lots of food.

_____

5. VAGUE ←————————————————————→ SHARP

We all watched as the group danced on stage.

_____

6. VAGUE ←————————————————————→ SHARP

I couldn't go to the event because I had too much work to do.

_____

7. VAGUE ←————————————————————→ SHARP

Serena always has the right accessories to match her outfits.

_____

8. VAGUE ←————————————————————→ SHARP

They attended a performance in the city.

_____

Add Snapshots and Thoughtshots

Snapshots	Thoughtshots
• Where were you?	• How did you feel while you were there?
• Was anyone else with you? Who?	• Did you want to get away or stay there?
• What time was it?	• What were you thinking about?
• Did you see anything unusual? What was it?	

1. **Read the skimpy story below. Then expand it with Snapshots and Thoughtshots.**

Where were you?

How did you feel?

The Race

The race was almost ready to begin. I looked around at the crowd. Then, the race started, and I was off! I tried to pace myself. I didn't want to use up all my energy. I didn't win the race, but I came in third.

Did you see anything unusual? What was it?

What were you thinking about?

_____

_____

_____

_____

_____

_____

_____

_____

_____

_____

_____

Add Snapshots and Thoughtshots, continued

2. Read the skimpy story below. Then expand it with Snapshots and Thoughtshots.

> ## The Test
> The day of the test had arrived. I went to bed early to rest my brain. The answers were in my head. I just had to remember them. I got up and ate some food. I was ready to go.

_____

_____

_____

_____

_____

_____

_____

_____

_____

_____

_____

_____

_____

_____

_____

_____

_____

_____

_____

Get on Target

Use the target diagram to plan a description of an event. Choose from the story ideas in the box or use one of your own.

Story Ideas

- The most interesting person you have ever met.
- A favorite childhood memory.
- The scariest thing that ever happened to you.
- The proudest moment in your life.

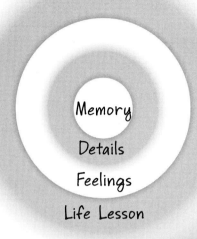

Memory

Details

Feelings

Life Lesson

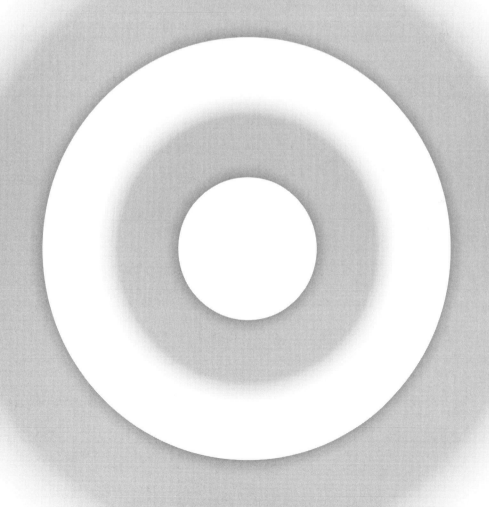

Get on Target, continued

Now write the story that you planned on page 117.

Add Meat to the Bones

Choose a bare-bones sentence from the list below. Write down details you can use to bring the moment to life.

> ### Bare-Bones Sentences
>
> - I fell off my skateboard in the middle of the parking lot.
> - Under the picnic table, I saw the biggest critter ever.
> - While eating spaghetti, I got sauce all over my white shirt.

Bare-Bones Sentence: _____

Dialogue What did you say? What did others say?	_____ _____ _____ _____ _____
Sensory Details What did you see? What did you hear? What did you smell?	_____ _____ _____ _____ _____
Snapshots Where were you? What could you see? What could you tell from looking around you?	_____ _____ _____ _____ _____
Thoughtshots How did you feel? Did you want to get away or stay? What were you thinking before, during, or after it happened?	_____ _____ _____ _____ _____

Add Meat to the Bones, continued

Use your chart from page 119 to write a developed, detailed paragraph.

Use your chart from page 119 to write a developed, detailed paragraph.

Checklist

- ☐ Include dialogue between characters.
- ☐ Use sensory details to help your reader imagine the scene.
- ☐ Give a complete description of everything in the scene.
- ☐ Tell what you were thinking and feeling.

Add Meat to the Bones, continued

Choose a different bare-bones sentence from page 119, or write one of your own. Write down details you can use to bring the moment to life.

Bare-Bones Sentence: _____

Dialogue What did you say? What did others say?	_____ _____ _____ _____ _____
Sensory Details What did you see? What did you hear? What did you smell?	_____ _____ _____ _____ _____ _____
Snapshots Where were you? What could you see? What could you tell from looking around you?	_____ _____ _____ _____ _____ _____
Thoughtshots How did you feel? Did you want to get away or stay? What were you thinking before, during, or after it happened?	_____ _____ _____ _____ _____

Add Meat to the Bones, continued

Use your chart from page 121 to write a developed, detailed paragraph.

Checklist

- ☐ Include dialogue between characters.
- ☐ Use sensory details to help your reader imagine the scene.
- ☐ Give a complete description of everything in the scene.
- ☐ Tell what you were thinking and feeling.

Zero In on a Moment

Choose a photo and tell a story about it on the index cards on page 124.

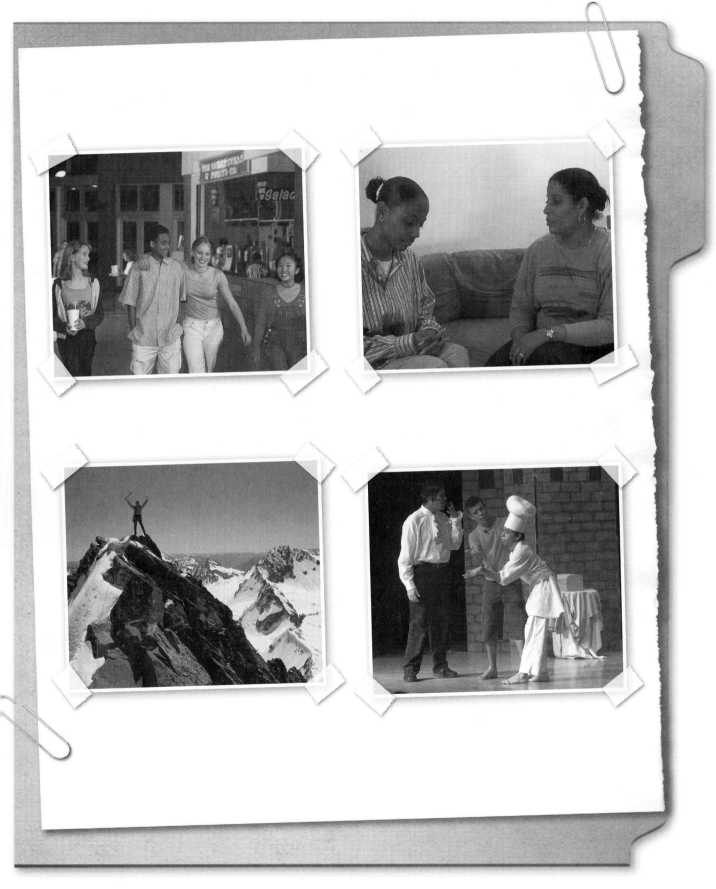

Write one event from the story on each index card.

Zero In on a Moment, continued

Circle the card on page 124 that shows your favorite moment.
Focus on that moment and "explode" it with details.

Checklist

- ❏ In one sentence, summarize everything that happened before this moment.
- ❏ Explode the moment by describing it in detail.
- ❏ Sum up what happened afterward in one sentence.

_____

_____

_____

_____

_____

_____

_____

_____

_____

_____

_____

_____

_____

_____

_____

_____

_____

_____

_____

_____

_____

_____

_____

_____

_____

_____

_____

_____

Zero In on a Moment, continued

Now choose a different moment from page 124. Focus on that moment and "explode" it with details.

Checklist

❑ In one sentence, summarize everything that happened before this moment.

❑ Explode the moment by describing it in detail.

❑ Sum up what happened afterward in one sentence.

_____

_____

_____

_____

_____

_____

_____

_____

_____

_____

_____

_____

_____

_____

_____

_____

_____

_____

_____

_____

_____

_____

_____

_____

_____

_____

Take Out Throwaway Writing

Underline or highlight the throwaway writing in this essay. Then condense into one paragraph the substance of what the student has said.

What to Drive

In this essay, my assignment is to write about different kinds of cars and trucks that people buy. Here's what I think. It is my belief that people should buy whichever kind of vehicle they want. But I also think people should not complain about gas prices.

Now I will tell you about my personal preference. I hope to own a hybrid car someday. I also hope that more people will buy hybrid cars. Let me explain the reasons behind my opinion. Hybrid cars use less gas and are better for the environment. In contrast, I consider driving a large, gas-guzzling vehicle to be wasteful.

In this paper, I discussed the different kinds of vehicles that are available. I hope you will consider the environment when you purchase your next vehicle. Thank you for reading my essay.

_____

_____

_____

_____

_____

_____

_____

_____

_____

_____

Underline or highlight the throwaway writing in this essay. Then condense what's left into one paragraph.

Dear Principal Edmondson:

First, I want to explain why I am writing you a letter. I am writing you a letter because I have heard many students complaining about the parking situation at our school. In my opinion, their complaints are justified.

Secondly, I want to ask what you think should be done to expand the number of parking spaces available. I'm sure you are a reasonable person who can find a way to solve this problem.

There is one more thing I would like to add. I must point out that many students are late for class because they have to walk from a parking space that is far away.

Please consider this as a serious subject. Thank you for reading my letter.

Sincerely,

Jon McCourt

Jon McCourt

Use Fewer Words

Revise each paragraph below to cut out the "deadwood." Use
revising marks. Be prepared to explain why a word or phrase you
deleted is unnecessary.

Revising Mark	What It Means
∧	Insert something.
⌇	Move to here.
⌅―	Replace with this.
℘	Take out.
∼	Transpose or reverse order.

1.

My friend Jorge is a really good guy. The reason why
I think he's a good guy is that he would do anything for
the people he cares about. I recall one memorable occasion very well.
My car broke down during a blizzard and I was stranded, with no way
to get home. Jorge helped me out by coming to pick me up.

2.

Prior to the beginning of the school year, Rashad went to a local
retailer to buy some new clothes. Unfortunately, his finances were rather
tight at that point in time. However, in spite of that fact, he was able to
find some good bargains so that he could start the school year in style.

3.

Jake's birthday was coming up soon. His girlfriend Casey was
wondering what to get him for a birthday gift. Due to the fact that she
had been very busy, she hadn't had much time to think about the matter.
Now that Jake's birthday was around the corner, finding the right gift had
suddenly become an urgent priority.

Write Tight

Choose a topic from the list or pick your own topic. Use all the space below to write a paragraph.

Write-Tight Topics

- a difficult relationship
- dealing with a long-distance romance
- managing schoolwork and your social life

Now rewrite the paragraph to make it tight. Make every word count.

Vary Your Sentences

Rewrite each paragraph using the Recipe for Sentence Variety.

Recipe for Sentence Variety
• Keep some sentences short and sweet.
• Craft some longer, "meaty" sentences, too.
• Consider adding a fragment or two—but don't overuse them.

1.

The community center was hosting a fall festival, and I wanted to help. Everyone likes my chocolate-chip cookies, so I decided to bake a few batches. I bought all of the ingredients, but I forgot one. I was mixing everything together, and then I realized I was missing the walnuts. I had to hurry back to the store so I could finish the cookies in time.

_____
_____
_____
_____
_____
_____
_____
_____
_____
_____
_____
_____
_____
_____
_____
_____
_____
_____

2.

> Our baseball team needed some new equipment. Our gloves and bats were getting worn down. We decided to have a car wash to raise some money. We held the car wash at a local car dealership. Everyone on the team volunteered to work. The car wash was a success. We raised a lot of money. We will probably have another car wash sometime soon.

Spice Up Your Verbs

Look at the photo and read the paragraph. Rewrite the paragraph, replacing the general verbs with more vivid ones.

The Best Vacation

My family and I **went** to Mexico for vacation last year. One night, we **had** dinner at a great restaurant near the beach. Mariachi musicians **walked** around. We **saw** dancers performing on a stage. They **moved** around in colorful costumes. It was great to look past the dancers and **see** the ocean. When the waiter came to our table, I ordered a quesadilla. Loud music and enticing aromas **filled** the air. My family and I **laughed** and **talked**. I **thought**, "This is one of the best vacations ever."

_____

_____

_____

_____

_____

_____

_____

_____

_____

_____

_____

Look at each photo below. Describe the scene using vivid verbs.

_____

_____

_____

_____

_____

_____

_____

_____

_____

_____

_____

_____

_____

_____

_____

_____

_____

_____

_____

_____

_____

_____

_____

_____

_____

_____

_____

Add Details with Prepositions

Use prepositional phrases to add details to each paragraph.

Some Prepositions

about	after	around	between	from	on	under
above	against	before	down	in	toward	until
across	among	beside	for	into	through	with

1.

> The fall festival was crowded. There were many different foods. Many people were selling crafts, too. I rode the rides. The Ferris wheel was fun. I could see everything.

The fall festival at the park near the river was crowded.

_____

_____

_____

_____

_____

_____

2.

> Jean loves pasta. She cooks many kinds. She actually has a special cabinet in her kitchen. Jean also makes her own sauce. She sells her sauce at local festivals.

_____

_____

_____

_____

_____

_____

_____

Place the Modifier

Add the modifier in the box to each sentence. Try different placements to see which adds the most punch to your sentence.

1. | nervously | Mahmoud waited in the gym, wondering whether he'd made the team.

   Nervously, Mahmoud waited in the gym, wondering whether he'd made the team.

2. | worn-out | Mahmoud looked around the gym and grabbed a basketball from his gym bag.

_____

3. | energetically | He began to shoot hoops.

_____

4. | ominous | The door swung open, Coach Rogers stood in the doorway.

_____

5. | briskly | He walked toward Mahmoud.

_____

6. | awkwardly | "Hi, Coach Rogers," Mahmoud said as he dribbled the ball.

_____

7. | confident | "We need you to play a game Saturday," Coach Rogers said with a smile.

_____

8. | excitedly | Mahmoud grabbed the basketball and shot a goal.

_____

Elaborate with Participles

Use participles or participial phrases to elaborate on each sentence. Try different placements to see which adds the most punch to your sentence.

1. Julia and I went downtown to shop.

Excited about the day ahead, Julia and I went downtown to shop.

_____

2. We had the best time in the music store.

_____

_____

3. I found lots of music that I'd heard on the radio.

_____

_____

4. Julia bought a CD.

_____

_____

5. I noticed that we missed our bus.

_____

_____

6. I was getting a little worried.

_____

_____

7. We saw one of our friends getting into her car.

_____

_____

8. We called out her name.

_____

_____

Elaborate with Clauses

Add an adjective clause and adverb clause to each sentence.

Adjective Clauses
Begin with a word like *who*, *that*, *which*, or *where* and modify a noun.

Adverb Clauses
Begin with a word like *after*, *before*, *if*, or *because* and modify a verb.

1. **Mandy** loves to **ride** her bike.

   Mandy, who is an expert cyclist, loves to ride her
   bike after she gets home from school every day.

2. Her **friends asked** her if she would like to go mountain biking with them.

   _____

   _____

3. She **decided** to try to ride the **mountain**.

   _____

   _____

4. Mandy and her **friends** entered the park and **pedaled** downhill.

   _____

   _____

5. She was **riding** her **bike** well.

   _____

   _____

6. Then they **reached** the **path** that leads to the summit.

   _____

   _____

7. **Mandy** was **scared** but took the challenge.

   _____

   _____

8. She **inhaled** deeply and began the steep journey up the **mountain**.

   _____

   _____

Elaborate with Absolutes

Use absolutes to combine the sentences.

1. His face was dripping with sweat. Benito waited for the whistle to sound.

   <u>His face dripping with sweat, Benito waited for the</u>
   <u>whistle to sound.</u>

2. His racket was feeling heavy. He kept telling himself the game was almost over.

   _____

   _____

3. The crowd was getting restless. They stared down at him from the stadium seats.

   _____

   _____

4. His fingers were wrapped tightly around his racket. His body was tingling with excitement.

   _____

   _____

5. His friends were chanting his name. They stood up and waved.

   _____

   _____

6. His eyes were focusing on the birds on the court. He thought how nice it would be to fly away.

   _____

   _____

7. The umpires were ready to blow the whistle. They announced the tied score one last time.

   _____

   _____

8. His heart was racing. Benito heard the whistle echo throughout the stadium.

   _____

   _____

No More Boring Writing!

Use all of the techniques you have learned to improve the boring paragraph.

How to Fix Boring Writing
- Vary your sentences.
- Use vivid verbs.
- Add modifiers in unusual places.
- Add details with prepositional phrases, participles, adjective and adverb clauses, and absolutes.

It was Saturday morning, and Jennifer's painting class was waiting for a bus to take them to New York City. Jennifer's teacher was from New York. She was excited to show the class several art galleries. The bus arrived. Jennifer had never been to the city, but she had read a lot about it. The trip took about three hours, but everyone was talking and laughing. The time went by very fast. Jennifer's stomach felt uneasy as the bus came to a stop. She was nervous and excited.

_____

_____

_____

_____

_____

_____

_____

_____

_____

_____

_____

_____

_____

Reflective Essay: Trap Family Memories

What experiences make up your family's unique history? Use page 141 to trap family memories.

1. Find a photograph that represents a memorable family moment. Write about it.

This photograph shows _____

_____

_____

_____

_____

2. One of the funniest things that ever happened to my family was _____

_____

_____

_____

_____

3. My family went through a rough time when _____

_____

_____

_____

_____

Reflective Essay: Analyze a Model

What makes this reflective essay a good model? Read the essay and answer the questions.

At a Glance

A good reflective essay
- captures readers' attention right away
- uses sensory details to bring memory alive
- connects ideas effectively with transitions
- allows the writer's voice to come through
- ends with a personal reflection.

A Great Time—Rain or Shine

"Gray and rainy" are not the first words that come to most people's minds when they think of their ideal summer vacation. Yet that's what the weather was like when my family stayed at my aunt Marisa's shore house last year —a trip that ended up being one of our best vacations ever.

We arrived on a clear, breezy Saturday. My brother and I barely waited to unpack before grabbing a few brightly colored towels and heading for the beach. Later, we were glad we'd made the most of that sunny afternoon.

I awoke the next morning to the sound of thunderclaps. The ocean was choppy, and the sky was an eerie, freaky shade of green. Soon it started pouring rain. My family and I didn't let that faze us, though. We spent the whole day playing cards and talking.

That night, I helped my aunt cook some fresh crabs for dinner. My cousins and I were laughing hysterically as we struggled to crack open the crab legs and get at the succulent shreds of meat inside. Over the next few days, we rented movies and played games with the younger kids. Despite the rain, we were having an awesome time.

The weather finally cleared up on Thursday, and I surfed and sunbathed like I do every year. I realize now that that's not the best part of the trip, though. Being with my family is.

How does the opening paragraph get readers' attention?

_____

_____

_____

_____

What sensory details bring the writer's experience to life?

_____

_____

_____

_____

Read the underlined sentences. How would you describe this writer's voice?

_____

_____

Which words make the writer's voice come through?

_____

_____

_____

_____

Why is the conclusion effective?

_____

_____

_____

_____

Plan a Reflective Essay

Use pages 143–144 to plan your reflective essay.

1. Choose a memory. What family experience will you write about and why?

_____

_____

_____

_____

2. Use the Five-Senses Diagram to trap the unforgettable ideas.

I saw . . .
I heard . . .
I smelled . . .
I tasted . . .
I touched/felt . . .

3. Use this space to plan how your ideas will flow. Write down words or phrases that describe the most unforgettable parts of the memory.

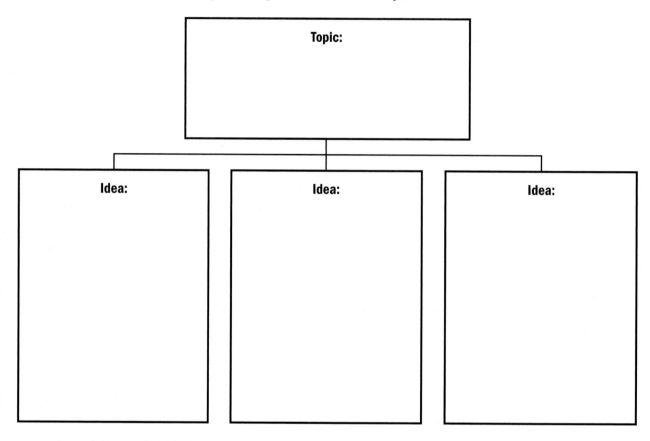

4. Ready to start writing? Try writing some beginning sentences that will make your reader want to find out more!

_____

_____

_____

_____

_____

_____

_____

_____

_____

_____

_____

_____

_____

_____

Reflective Essay: First Draft

Use your plan from pages 143–144 to write the first draft of your
reflective essay. Be sure to tell the story in your own voice.

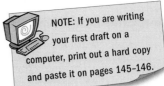

NOTE: If you are writing
your first draft on a
computer, print out a hard copy
and paste it on pages 145–146.

Drafting Checklist

- ❏ Capture the readers' interest with your introduction.
- ❏ Include sensory details.
- ❏ Connect ideas with transitions.
- ❏ Let your voice come through.
- ❏ End by reflecting on the memory.

Reflective Essay: First Draft, continued

Reflective Essay: Revised Draft

Use the checklist to revise your first draft on pages 145–146.
Incorporate all your changes on pages 147–148.

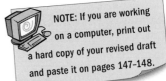

NOTE: If you are working on a computer, print out a hard copy of your revised draft and paste it on pages 147–148.

Revising Checklist

- [ ] How can you make your introduction more interesting?
- [ ] Can you think of more sensory details to include?
- [ ] Did you use transitions to make the ideas flow smoothly?
- [ ] Do the ideas flow smoothly? Do you need to add some transitions?
- [ ] Is the personal reflection at the end effective? How can you improve it?

Letter of Problem Solving: Solve the Problem

Think about problems you have had as a consumer. Describe each problem, and then list a possible solution.

Problem:

For my mom's birthday present, I ordered a book online—but the company sent the wrong book to my house.

Solution:

I could send the book back to the company with a letter explaining that it isn't what I ordered.

Problem:

_____

_____

Solution:

_____

_____

_____

_____

Problem:

_____

_____

Solution:

_____

_____

_____

_____

Letter of Problem Solving: Analyze a Model

What makes this letter of problem solving a good model? Read the letter and answer the questions.

At a Glance

A good letter of problem solving

- is formatted as a business letter
- is addressed to a specific person, when possible
- includes all necessary facts about the problem
- proposes a solution
- sounds firm but polite.

219 Walnut Drive
Philadelphia, PA 19120
(215) 555-9820
September 19, 2007

Ms. Gina Sanchez
Customer Service Representative
Bright Gamez, Inc.
5000 State Street
Santa Fe, NM 87505

Dear Ms. Sanchez:

On August 28, 2007, I purchased a "Total Tackle" video game from the Bright Gamez Web site. My friends and I looked forward to playing it.

After my game arrived, I tried to play it with my friends, but the graphics on the screen kept fading out. As a result, we were unable to enjoy the game.

I am enclosing the video game and a copy of my receipt. Please send me a new copy of "Total Tackle" as soon as possible.

Thank you for your attention to this matter. If you have any questions, please contact me at (215) 555-9820.

Sincerely,

Bryan Forester

Bryan Forester

What details show that this is a business letter?

_____

_____

_____

Why did the writer address the letter to Ms. Sanchez?

_____

_____

_____

_____

What specific details does the writer include about the problem?

_____

_____

_____

_____

What solution does the writer propose?

_____

_____

_____

_____

Underline examples of the writer's polite tone. Why is this tone effective?

_____

_____

_____

Plan a Letter of Problem Solving

Select one of the problems you wrote about on page 149.
Use pages 151–152 to plan your letter.

1. Call the company or check their Web site to find out who handles customer complaints. Record the name and address of the person you plan to write to.

_____

_____

_____

_____

2. Plan your letter. Use the chart to organize your facts.

What did I buy?
When did I buy it?
Where did I buy it?
What was the problem?
Why was it a problem?

3. Propose two possible solutions to the problem. Be specific. Then include the information that the company will need to carry out the solution.

SOLUTION	What specific information will the company need to carry out this solution?

Which solution would you prefer? Why?

_____

_____

_____

4. Ready to start writing? When you write a letter of problem solving, getting the right tone can be tricky. Practice first by rewriting the sentences below.

I would kind of appreciate it if you could send me a refund for $24.99.

Please send me a refund in the amount of $24.99.

I feel totally ripped off. You'd better send me a replacement right away!

_____

_____

_____

If it's not too much trouble, please issue me a refund or store credit for $17.51.

_____

_____

_____

Letter of Problem Solving:
First Draft

Use your plan from pages 151–152 to write the first draft of your letter.

NOTE: If you are writing your first draft on a computer, print out a hard copy and paste it on page 153.

Drafting Checklist

- [ ] Use a business-letter format.
- [ ] Write to a specific person, if possible.
- [ ] Include all of the necessary facts about the problem.
- [ ] Propose a solution to the problem.
- [ ] Be polite but firm.

Letter of Problem Solving: Revised Draft

Use the checklist to revise your first draft on page 153.
Incorporate all your changes on page 154.

NOTE: If you are working on a computer, print out a hard copy of your revised draft and paste it on page 154.

Revising Checklist

- ❑ Do you need to include more details about the problem?

- ❑ Do you need to make clear exactly how you'd like to solve the problem?

- ❑ Are you satisfied that your tone is polite but firm? What changes can you make?

Short, Short Story: Invent a Story

Look at the pictures below. On page 156, invent a story to go with the pictures.

Short, Short Story: Analyze a Model

What makes this short, short story a good model? Read the story and answer the questions. (The story continues on page 158.)

(The story continues on page 158.)

At a Glance

A good short, short story

- begins by quickly introducing the setting
- develops the characters with a few key details and dialogue
- focuses on the plot: a brief series of events with a turning point
- ends by telling how a character changes or how a problem is resolved.

The Woods

It was a chilly weekend in November. Devon Blackwell and his friends, Louis and T.J., had planned a camping trip at a distant West Virginia campsite near an old, supposedly haunted Civil War battleground. Devon had turned 17 that summer, so he agreed to drive. Three hours and ten hamburgers later, they arrived.

"I want to go see the battleground," Louis said.

"Actually, I think we should get our camping stuff set up before the sun goes down. I bet it gets really dark around here at night," T.J. replied.

"What, are you afraid some old Civil War ghost will get you?" Devon joked. "We still have three hours before sunset. Let's go look around." Devon wanted to stretch after the long car ride.

"You guys go ahead, but I'm staying and setting up our stuff," said T.J. "Come back and get me in an hour."

"He just needs to relax," Devon muttered as they walked toward the old battleground.

"Seriously," agreed Louis. "Maybe he really is weirded out by this place. I guess it is a little spooky."

"I bet it's pretty creepy at night," said Devon. "Especially if you're the kind of person who gets all uptight and anxious over every little thing…" A slow smile spread across his face.

How is the setting important to the story?

_____

_____

_____

_____

What does the dialogue reveal about each of the characters?

_____

_____

_____

_____

_____

_____

_____

_____

_____

What is the main conflict in this story?

_____

_____

_____

_____

_____

_____

_____

_____

Louis had seen that smile before. He knew what it meant. "Are you thinking what I'm thinking?" he asked.

"You bet."

Meanwhile, T.J. was busy at the campsite. An hour passed, then two. His friends were nowhere to be seen. When the sun crept behind the mountain, T.J. built a fire.

As the sky grew dark, he started to worry. Then he heard a crackling sound. *Must be a raccoon or something,* he told himself.

Suddenly a light appeared and began moving toward him. Two lights, actually, seeming to glow yellow in the dark. They looked like the eyes of an owl, staring at him. The crackling sounds grew closer.

As T.J. warily stepped back toward his tent, Devon couldn't contain himself any longer. His laughter echoed through the woods. "Dude, that was priceless!" he howled.

Louis pulled the flashlight out from underneath his ski cap and shined it on T.J.'s face. "Sorry, man, but the look on your face just now was pretty funny," Louis said.

"I'm glad I could entertain you," T.J. said dryly. Just then Louis's flashlight went out.

"Hey, T.J.,... you packed extra batteries and stuff, right?" Louis asked.

"Of course," his friend replied. "After all, *someone's* gotta be the responsible one around here."

Circle the paragraph that contains the turning point of the story.

How is the conflict between T.J. and his friends resolved?

_____

_____

_____

_____

_____

_____

_____

_____

_____

_____

_____

_____

Plan a Short, Short Story

Use pages 159–160 to plan your story.

1. Consider your audience and purpose. Is your story for adults, other teens, or children? What emotional response do you want to create?

_____

_____

_____

2. Plan your plot. Use the flowchart to sketch out the main events in your story.

Beginning

↓

Before the Turning Point

↓

Turning Point

↓

After the Turning Point

↓

End (Resolution)

3. Now that you have the "skeleton" of your story, flesh it out with key details about the setting and characters.

SETTING
Time:
Place:
Key descriptive details:

CHARACTERS		
Name	**Detail about Character**	**What It Reveals**

4. Decide whose "voice" will tell the story. (If the narrator is a character, use first-person. If the narrator is not a character, use third-person.)

Short, Short Story: First Draft

Use your plan from pages 159–160 to write the first draft of your story.

NOTE: If you are writing your first draft on a computer, print out a hard copy and paste it on pages 161–162.

Drafting Checklist

- ❏ Establish the setting and characters with just a few details.
- ❏ Develop characters further with dialogue.
- ❏ Keep the focus on the plot. Include a turning point.
- ❏ Tell how the problem is resolved.

Short, Short Story: Revised Draft

Use the checklist to revise your first draft on pages 161–162.
Incorporate all the changes on pages 163–164.

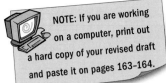

NOTE: If you are working on a computer, print out a hard copy of your revised draft and paste it on pages 163–164.

Revising Checklist

- ❏ Are the setting and characters clearly introduced at the beginning?
- ❏ What dialogue or details can you add to make the characters come alive?
- ❏ What transition words or phrases can you add to make the order of events clearer?
- ❏ Do you need to add more details to the resolution?

Persuasive Essay: What Do You Think?

**Briefly explain whether you agree or disagree with each statement.
Give reasons for your position.**

1. Families shouldn't give teenagers an allowance. Teens should earn their spending money by working part-time.

   _____

   _____

   _____

   _____

2. Requiring students to wear uniforms would improve life at our school.

   _____

   _____

   _____

   _____

3. Teenagers should stay informed about politics and current events. Even if you're not old enough to vote, you should know what's going on in the world.

   _____

   _____

   _____

   _____

4. No one under the age of 18 should be allowed to drive.

   _____

   _____

   _____

   _____

5. School starts too early in the morning. High school students should have classes from 9 to 4.

   _____

   _____

   _____

   _____

Persuasive Essay: Analyze a Model

What makes this persuasive essay a good model? Read the essay carefully and answer the questions.

A good persuasive essay
- introduces the writer's position with a thesis statement
- supports the position with reasons and evidence
- appeals to readers' emotions without sounding extreme
- acknowledges opposing points of view
- ends with a call to action.

Healthier Lunches for Taylor High

"You should eat a balanced diet with lots of fruits and vegetables." We've all heard this recommendation, but most teenagers don't follow it. One reason is that school cafeterias often serve unhealthy meals. I think our school should promote better eating habits by serving healthier lunches.

A quick look at our menus shows that nutrition is not a priority. This week's meals include hamburgers, Philly cheese steaks, and pepperoni pizza—all foods that are high in fat, salt, and cholesterol. With juvenile obesity on the rise, our cafeteria needs to provide better options.

Many students at Taylor High agree that our school lunches need an overhaul. Varsity basketball player Melissa Bart explains, "If I eat junk for lunch, I have no energy during practice. I wish the cafeteria offered healthier foods." Offering healthier foods would not only improve students' health, it also might help them to be more energetic and alert. Improving school lunches could lead to improvements in students' academic performance.

Some people will say that students are responsible for their own health and well-being. That's true, but school officials can help by encouraging students to make good choices. I urge the students of Taylor High to petition our principal and request healthier school lunches.

Underline the writer's thesis statement.

List two reasons the writer gives for her position.

_____

_____

_____

_____

_____

List three examples of evidence the writer uses to support the arguments.

_____

_____

_____

_____

_____

_____

Underline the sentence where the writer acknowledges an opposing point of view on this issue.

What call to action does the writer include?

_____

_____

_____

Plan a Persuasive Essay

Use pages 167–168 to plan your persuasive essay.

1. Choose an issue you know and care about. You can use one of the issues on page 165. Briefly state your position. Describe what people should do about the issue and why.

_____

_____

_____

2. In the chart below, gather facts and details to support your arguments. You might include personal examples, facts, statistics, and experts' opinions.

Argument	Evidence

3. Organize your main supporting points in order of importance.

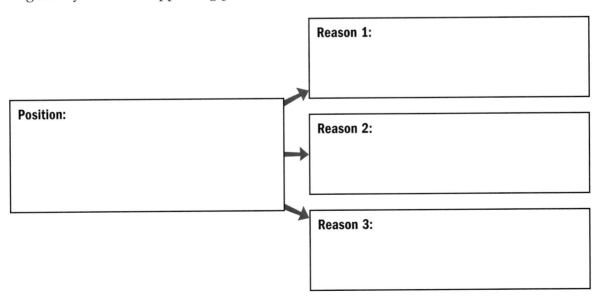

Position:

Reason 1:

Reason 2:

Reason 3:

Plan a Persuasive Essay, continued

4. Anticipate the most likely objections to your arguments. Plan how you will rebut, or disprove, these objections.

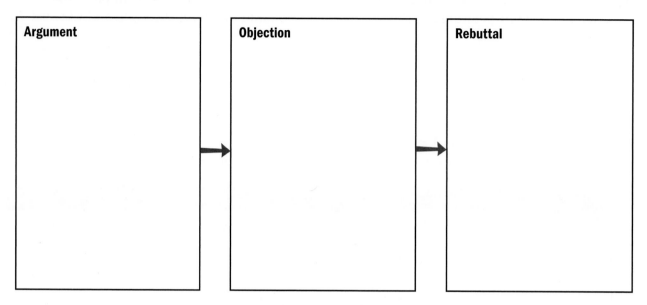

Argument	Objection	Rebuttal

5. Ready to start writing? Practice using persuasive language effectively. Rewrite the following sentences so they appeal to readers' emotions without sounding harsh.

Many high school students are not very alert during their first-period classes.

Many high school students struggle to stay awake during their first-period classes.

Our democracy depends on *everyone's* participation! If you're too lazy to vote, then you have no right to complain about anything the government does.

_____

_____

_____

Some of my friends hate the idea of dressing like a clone. They have no use for lame school uniforms.

_____

_____

_____

Giving teenagers an allowance just turns them into selfish, spoiled brats who depend on their parents for handouts.

_____

_____

_____

Persuasive Essay: First Draft

Use your plan from pages 167–168 to write the first draft of your persuasive essay.

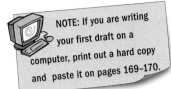

NOTE: If you are writing your first draft on a computer, print out a hard copy and paste it on pages 169–170.

Drafting Checklist

- ❏ Introduce your position in your thesis.
- ❏ Support your position with reasons and evidence.
- ❏ Appeal to readers' emotions with persuasive language.
- ❏ Address other points of view.
- ❏ End with a call to action.

Persuasive Essay: Revised Draft

Use the checklist to revise your first draft on pages 169–170.
Incorporate all your changes on pages 171–172.

NOTE: If you are working on a computer, print out a hard copy of your revised draft and paste it on pages 171–172.

Revising Checklist

- ❏ How can you make your thesis statement more clear and impactful?

- ❏ Does your argument sound convincing? Do you need to add better reasons or more support?

- ❏ Is your language too bland, too emotional, or just right? What can you do to improve the tone?

- ❏ How can you make your call to action simpler and clearer?

Persuasive Essay: Revised Draft, continued

Literary Critique: State Your Opinion

What have you read recently, for school or for your own enjoyment? How did you like it? Think about your opinions of what you've read.

1. List several works of literature you have read recently—fiction, nonfiction, or poetry—that you have strong opinions about.

_____

_____

_____

_____

2. Choose one work and write a note to a friend explaining why he or she should or should not read it. Don't worry about "proving" your opinion. Just get it down on paper.

_____

_____

_____

_____

3. Jot down three quotations from this work. Choose quotations that are important to understanding the work as a whole.

_____

_____

_____

_____

_____

_____

_____

_____

_____

_____

Literary Critique:
Analyze a Model

What makes this literary critique a good model? Read the critique carefully and answer the questions.

At a Glance

A good literary critique

- hooks the reader at the start with an interesting detail, and gives the work's title and author
- clearly states the writer's opinion
- supports opinions with details and direct quotations
- presents a balanced point of view
- ends by restating the writer's opinion.

The Agony of Adolescence

High school is difficult for most teenagers, but it's especially tough if you're only four-foot-two. Andrew Auseon's novel *Funny Little Monkey* describes the struggles of Arty, a brainy, abnormally tiny 14-year-old whose oversized twin brother beats him up on a regular basis. I highly recommend this novel to any teenager who, like Arty, constantly feels like a misfit.

In depicting Arty's life, Auseon captures the reality of high school through his colorful language. While sitting in class one day, Arty muses, "Only one window remains clear and bright, providing the cave beasts and mutants among us a rare glimpse of the outside world." When Arty teams up with the school's other social outcasts to get revenge on his brother, his life takes a turn for the better—but it also gets weirder. In the process, he also gets a girlfriend of sorts—smart, sarcastic Leslie Dermott, who breaks all of the unwritten rules of High School Survival 101.

Although the book's plot is occasionally farfetched, I still enjoyed the story from start to finish. Auseon's first novel captures the high school experience with sensitivity and humor. It also gets an important message across: If you are different in any way, high school is tough, but in the end, it is important to embrace the qualities that make you unique. I strongly recommend this novel to any teenager who wonders why high school has to be so hard.

Underline the sentence that states the writer's overall opinion of the book.

Circle details that help to support the writer's opinions.

Why does the writer include the underlined sentence in his critique of the book?

_____

_____

_____

_____

_____

_____

_____

_____

In your own words, sum up the writer's opinion of the novel.

_____

_____

_____

_____

_____

_____

_____

_____

_____

_____

Plan a Literary Critique

Use pages 175–176 to plan your literary critique.

1. Write down the title and author of the work you want to critique. Skim through the work again as you complete the chart below.

Literature	
Opinions and reactions	

What's good about it?	**What could be better?**

Would I recommend this work to other people? Why or why not?

2. Now, think about how you'll back up your opinions. Gather specific details and direct quotations from the text that support your impressions.

OPINIONS	SUPPORTING EXAMPLES

Literary Critique: First Draft

Use your plan from pages 175–176 to write the first draft of your literary critique.

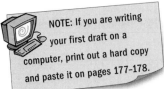

NOTE: If you are writing your first draft on a computer, print out a hard copy and paste it on pages 177–178.

Drafting Checklist

- ☐ Name the title and author, hook the reader with an interesting detail, and state your overall opinion.
- ☐ Support your opinions with details and direct quotations.
- ☐ Present a balanced point of view—don't rant or rave.
- ☐ End by restating your opinion. If you wish, include a personal reflection.

178

Literary Critique: Revised Draft

Use the checklist to revise your first draft on pages 177–178.
Incorporate all your changes on pages 179–180.

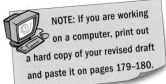

NOTE: If you are working on a computer, print out a hard copy of your revised draft and paste it on pages 179–180.

Revising Checklist

- ❏ How can you reword the introduction to get readers interested from the start?

- ❏ Do you need to include more evidence to support your opinion?

- ❏ How can you rework the ending to leave the reader with a balanced summary of your opinion?

Literary Critique: Revised Draft, continued

Résumé: Take Inventory

What do you have to offer an employer? Think about your interests, skills, and achievements as you complete the sentences below.

1. I'm really good at _____

_____

_____

2. I would like to learn more about _____

_____

I'm interested in this because _____

_____

_____

3. My proudest moment was when _____

_____

This experience shows that I _____

_____

_____

4. If I could work at any job I chose, it would be _____

_____

I would like this job because _____

_____

_____

Résumé: Analyze a Model

What makes this résumé a good model?
Read the résumé and answer the questions.

Camp counselors needed at Hope Mtn. Day Camp. F/t. June 30-August 15. Duties include supervising campers aged 8-12, leading hikes, and ensuring safety during water activities.
Contact B. Webster, 555-0181.

At a Glance

A good résumé
- is tailored to what the employer is looking for
- begins with contact information, an objective, and a profile
- describes specific skills with strong verbs
- is organized in sections.

Joe Okami
231 15th Avenue, York, WA 98122
(206) 555-3948
jokami@hikerbike.com

OBJECTIVE To work as a camp counselor at Hope Mountain Day Camp

PROFILE An athletic outdoorsman experienced in working with kids

EXPERIENCE AND RELATED ACTIVITIES

York Township Community Pool
Lifeguard
(2005–2007, summers)

- Monitored pool users' safety

- Assisted in teaching children's swim classes

- Certified in CPR and first-aid

York High School Hiking Club
President (2005–2006)

- Organized weekend hikes (2003–2004)

EDUCATION
- Anticipated June 2007 graduation from York High School, York, WA

- Attending Hope Teachers' College in the fall of 2007

- Awarded full scholarship

Why is it important to include contact information?

_____

_____

_____

How does the writer tailor his résumé to what the employer is looking for?

_____

_____

_____

_____

_____

_____

Underline the active verbs that the writer uses to describe his experience.

What features give this résumé an organized, professional appearance?

_____

_____

_____

_____

_____

_____

_____

Plan a Résumé

Use pages 183–184 to plan your résumé.

1. Decide what kind of job you want. Write some possibilities below or paste in a Help Wanted ad that appeals to you.

_____

_____

_____

_____

2. Use your notes from page 181 to create a detailed inventory of your skills and accomplishments. Be honest, but emphasize the good things you have to offer.

PERSONAL INVENTORY	
Education	**Work Experience**
School Activities	**Hobbies**
Accomplishments/Honors	**Other**

3. Plan how you will organize the information in sections, using reverse chronological order in each section. Use the space below to sketch the layout of your résumé.

4. Ready to start writing? You can make your résumé stand out by using precise language and strong verbs. Practice by rewriting the phrases below.

Helped kids swim.

Supervised 12 campers in Olympic-sized pool.
_____

Worked at a restaurant.

_____

Worked as a volunteer in a nursing home.

_____

Now, describe one of your own work experiences using precise language:

_____
_____
_____

Résumé: First Draft

Use your plan from pages 183–184 to write the first draft of your résumé.

NOTE: If you are writing your first draft on a computer, print out a hard copy and paste it on page 185.

Drafting Checklist

- ☐ If you're applying for a specific job, tailor your résumé to the employer's needs.
- ☐ Include contact information, an objective, and a brief profile.
- ☐ Organize information into sections with headings.
- ☐ Use precise language and strong verbs.

Résumé: Revised Draft

Use the checklist to revise your first draft on page 185. Then keyboard it, format it neatly, and paste the hard copy here.

Use the checklist to revise your first draft on page 185.

Revising Checklist

- ❏ How can you reword the objective to better suit what the employer is looking for?
- ❏ How can you improve the organization of your experience and related activities?
- ❏ How can you better emphasize your skills and accomplishments?
- ❏ Do you need to include more specific language and vivid verbs?

News Article: Gather Ideas for Reporting

Jot down some ideas for articles you might write as a reporter. List topics that really interest you.

Topic	Article I Might Write
Civil Rights Movement leader Martin Luther King, Jr.	a commemoration of King's life and work
why arts funding was cut at our school	investigative article for my school newspaper

News Article:
Analyze a Model

What makes this news article a good model? Read the article carefully and answer the questions.

At a Glance

A good news article
- sums up the story in a concise headline
- tells who, what, where, when, and why
- gives the most important information first
- objectively presents the facts.

Bears Forfeit Wins Due to Teammates' Grades
by Emma Otts

1   Dec. 12—MADISON, WI—The Kenridge High Bears were forced to forfeit five recent football victories this week after Principal Manuel Torena discovered that some players do not meet the academic standards for student athletes.

2   While reviewing one player's transcript, Torena found that the student had a GPA of 1.7. Kenridge High School's academic standards require that students who participate in athletic events maintain a GPA of 2.0 or better.

3   Additional transcript checks revealed that two other football players did not meet academic eligibility requirements. The players' names are being withheld.

4   Principal Torena immediately contacted the Wisconsin High School Athletic Association to alert them of the oversight. According to WHSAA regulations, schools must forfeit any games in which an ineligible athlete participated. Additionally, Kenridge High School may face a fine and a one-year probation period during which all players' transcripts will be routinely checked by the WHSAA.

5   Since Kenridge High School voluntarily reported the oversight, the school will not face more severe consequences. Nevertheless, some players are upset by the decision.

State the main idea of the article.

_____

_____

_____

List the essential details the writer provides in the lead paragraph.

What: _____

_____

Who: _____

_____

Where: _____

_____

When: _____

_____

Why: _____

_____

How does the author achieve an objective tone? List examples that support your answer.

_____

_____

_____

_____

_____

_____

_____

_____

_____

News Article: Analyze a Model, continued

6   "Our team had a winning record, and now we won't make the playoffs," commented Bears quarterback Matt Pergoli. "It's so unfair that the entire team is being penalized for the school's mistake."

7   It is the responsibility of the school's athletic director to check each athlete's academic eligibility on a quarterly basis. Kenridge Athletic Director Greg Haas states that the mistake was unintentional. "We have so many student athletes at Kenridge that sometimes problems get overlooked," he explained. "But Principal Torena and I take this issue very seriously."

8   In addition to maintaining a GPA of 2.0 or higher, athletes at Kenridge High School must pass all six of their classes in order to remain eligible for sports. These classes include four core academic courses and two electives.

9   Some Wisconsin school districts are looking for ways to raise eligibility standards even higher. WHSAA Executive Director Roger Yee has suggested raising the minimum required GPA to 2.5 and checking students' averages on a monthly basis.

10   Keisha Davis, the basketball coach at nearby Martin High School, believes that students should focus on academics first, athletics second.

11   "There are only a handful of players who go on to have a professional career." she said. "Our students need to be prepared for a future that involves more than sports."

How are the quotes in paragraph 6 and 7 relevant to the article?

_____

_____

_____

_____

_____

_____

_____

_____

_____

_____

Does the article follow the Inverted Pyramid structure? Explain your answer.

_____

_____

_____

_____

_____

_____

_____

_____

_____

_____

_____

_____

Plan a News Article: Choose a Topic

1 Use this page to choose a topic for a news article and get down the basic facts.

Topic: _____

What Makes It Newsworthy:_____

_____

_____

_____

ANSWER THE 5 W'S	
WHAT **happened?**	
WHO **was involved?**	
WHERE **did it happen?**	
WHEN **did it happen?**	
WHY **did it happen?**	

News Article: Gather Information

2 Use this page to gather background for your news article. Write down sources you may want to look up or people you may want to interview. Then go get the facts!

_____

_____

_____

_____

_____

_____

_____

_____

_____

_____

_____

_____

_____

_____

_____

_____

_____

_____

_____

_____

_____

_____

_____

_____

_____

_____

_____

_____

News Article: Organize Information

3 Use the graphic below to plan how you'll organize your news article.

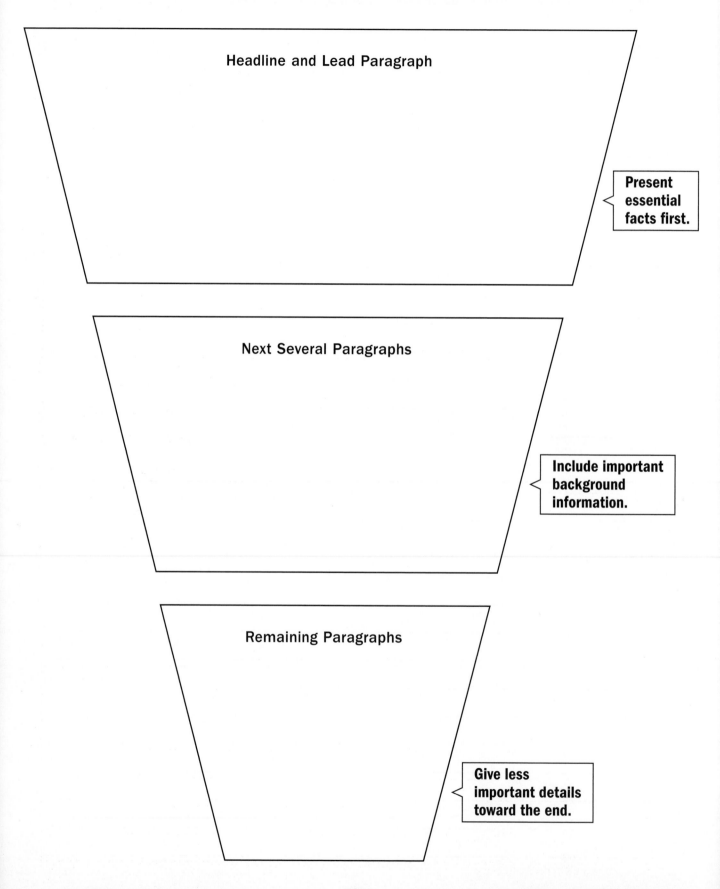

Headline and Lead Paragraph

Present essential facts first.

Next Several Paragraphs

Include important background information.

Remaining Paragraphs

Give less important details toward the end.

News Article: First Draft

Use pages 193–194 to draft your news article.

NOTE: If you are writing your first draft on a computer, print out a hard copy and paste it on pages 193–194.

Drafting Checklist

- ❏ Write a headline that gets the reader's attention and sums up the story.
- ❏ Present essential details in the lead paragraph.
- ❏ Flesh out the story with background information.
- ❏ Maintain an objective tone.
- ❏ End with relevant, but less important details.

194

News Article: Revised Draft

Use pages 195–196 to revise your news article.

NOTE: If you are working on a computer, print out a hard copy of your revised draft and paste it on pages 195–196.

Revising Checklist

- ❏ Can you improve your headline?
- ❏ How can you make your lead paragraph more concise?
- ❏ Where can you include more background information?
- ❏ Is your tone objective enough for a news article?

196

Poem in Free Verse: Get Inspired

A poem can be about anything. Use one of the photographs below for inspiration, or paste in a photo that's important to you. What feelings does the picture evoke?

IDEAS

_____
_____
_____
_____
_____
_____
_____
_____

_____
_____
_____
_____
_____
_____
_____

_____
_____
_____
_____
_____
_____
_____

Poem in Free Verse: Analyze a Model

What makes this poem a good model? Read the poem carefully and answer the questions.

At a Glance

A good free-verse poem
- focuses on a single image or emotion
- does not use a regular rhythm, traditional stanzas, or rhyme
- may break writing conventions of sentence structure and punctuation
- may use poetic devices such as figurative language, imagery, or repetition
- aims to produce a certain mood or feeling.

Sunrise in Vermont

I walk the tree-lined trail
in the early morning
before the moon descends

The grass gleams
from last night's rain shower
Blades shimmer as they sway in the breeze

This morning is magic
I walk until I reach the white mountain
where the sun slumbers—

Soon the snow will sing with light
be too strong for the unmasked eye
And I will turn back
toward the green of the trees

A quiet retreat
Before the moon descends
on the tree-lined trail.

What is the central idea of this poem?

_____

_____

_____

_____

List a few examples of poetic devices the writer uses (such as repetition).

_____

_____

_____

_____

_____

_____

What mood or feeling does this poem create? Explain your answer.

_____

_____

_____

_____

_____

Underline an example of the poem breaking conventions of punctuation.

Plan a Poem in Free Verse

Use pages 199–200 to plan your poem.

1 Choose a topic you feel deeply about. Use the graphic below to narrow your topic.

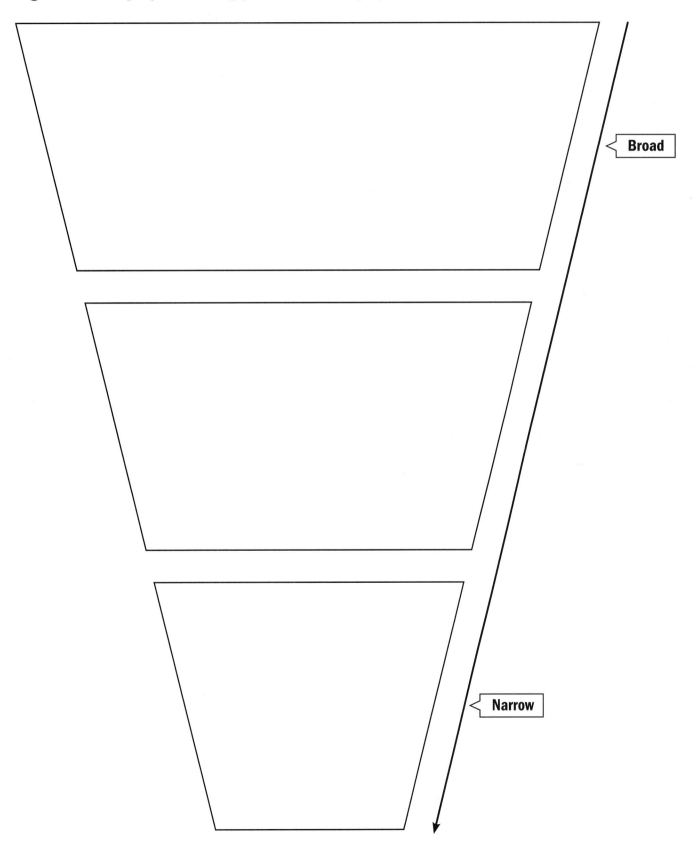

Broad

Narrow

Plan a Poem in Free Verse, continued

2 Jot down your ideas and impressions about the topic. Don't worry about using complete sentences—just brainstorm as many ideas as you can.

Poem in Free Verse: First Draft

Use this page to draft your poem.

NOTE: If you are writing your first draft on a computer, print out hard copy and paste it on page 201.

paste it on page 201.

Drafting Checklist

- ❏ Focus on a single image or emotion.
- ❏ Think about the mood or feeling you want to create.
- ❏ Play with the words and sounds.
- ❏ Try different versions until you land on one you like.
- ❏ It's okay to break conventions, but make sure your poem still makes sense.

Poem in Free Verse: Revised Draft

Use the checklist to revise the first draft of your poem. Write the revised draft here, incorporating all your changes.

NOTE: If you are working on a computer, print out hard copy of your revised draft and paste it on page 202.

Revising Checklist

☐ Read your poem aloud. Can you make changes to make it sound better?

☐ Which lines can you revise to increase your poem's emotional effect?

Research Report: Develop a Game Plan

Choose a research topic that interests you. Then work with a partner to narrow it so it's focused and specific.

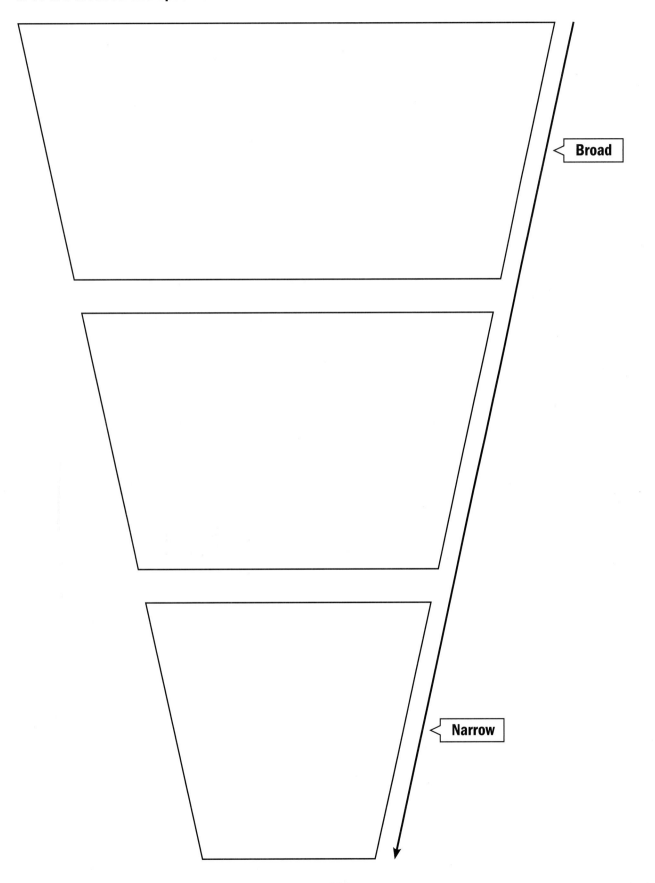

Broad

Narrow

Research Report: Develop a Game Plan, continued

Fill out the FATP chart to help you plan your paper. Then plan some research questions.

FATP Chart

Form: _research report_

Audience: _____

Topic: _____

Purpose: _____

Research Questions

Information Sources: Plan Your Search

Brainstorm some ideas for information sources you could use in your research. (If you can use the world around you for part of your research, jot down ideas for direct observation.)

_____

_____

_____

_____

_____

_____

_____

_____

Now list five interview questions you would ask an expert on your topic.

1. _____

_____

_____

2. _____

_____

_____

3. _____

_____

_____

4. _____

_____

_____

5. _____

_____

_____

Review the chart on page 439 of the *Good Writer's Guide.* **Choose three types of published sources that would be most helpful in your research. Explain why you chose each type.**

Type of Source: _____

_____

_____

Type of Source: _____

_____

_____

Type of Source: _____

_____

_____

Now use an online library catalog (or go to a library) and choose five published sources you might use for your research report. List the title (and author, if possible) of each source.

1. _____

_____

_____

2. _____

_____

_____

3. _____

_____

_____

4. _____

_____

_____

5. _____

_____

_____

Selecting Print Sources

**Study the selections from the table of contents and index of the same book.
Then answer the questions.**

CONTENTS

Introduction iv
1   The Digestive System 3
2   How the Digestive System Works 21
3   Common Disorders of the Digestive System 35
4   Digestive Disorders 51
5   A Look at the Research 89
6   Cancers of the Digestive System 101

Index

Duodenal ulcers
    symptoms, 89–90
    treatment, 91
Duodenum, 4, 93, 95, 97
Esophagitis
    causes, 56–61
    prevalence, 57
    treatments, 62–74
Esophagus, 5, 56, 59

Heartburn, 24–25
Hernia, 1–108
Intestines
    intestinal cancer, 115–123
    large intestine, 17, 48, 99–101
    small intestine, 16–18, 57, 63
Lactose
    inability to digest, 76–79

1. On what page would you find information about how common esophagitis is? _____

2. Would this book be useful for a research paper about treating lung cancer? Why or why not?

_____

_____

3. Where could you find information about people who cannot digest lactose?

_____

_____

4. How useful would this book be if you were writing a paper about duodenal ulcers?
Explain your answer.

_____

_____

5. Is this book likely to include lots of information about rare digestive disorders?
Why or why not?

_____

_____

207

Read the abstract for a scientific journal article. Then answer the questions.

Journal of Oncology, 9.2, October 2006

Preventing Bone-Density Loss in Cancer Patients
Ramon Gonzales, M.D

Abstract

Background In patients with breast, lung, and prostate cancer, it's common for the cancer to spread to their bones, resulting in pain and a loss of bone density. Zoledronic acid was used as an experimental treatment for these patients.

Methods Over a period of 10 months, 280 cancer patients were assigned to four groups. Three groups were given zoledronic acid in dosages of 4 mg, 2 mg, or 0.4 mg. Subjects in the remaining group received other treatments.

Results: Zoledronic acid slowed the rate of bone-density loss in subjects who received dosages of 2 mg or 4 mg. These subjects also reported lower levels of pain. No difference was seen in the other two groups.

Conclusions: Zoledronic acid in doses of 2 mg or greater slows bone-density loss and reduces pain.

1. According to the abstract, what types of cancer does this article discuss?

_____

_____

2. Would this journal article be useful to someone writing a research report on the known causes of lung cancer? Why or why not?

_____

_____

_____

_____

3. Would this article be useful to someone writing a research paper on treatments for cancer? Why or why not?

_____

_____

_____

_____

Now review the table of contents, index, and any abstracts in the published sources you listed as possibilities on page 206. Decide if any of them would really be helpful to you in research.

Evaluating Web Sites

Look at the two Web sites. Then answer the questions on page 210.

http://www.remmysgilamonsterpage.net

GilaMonster.com

Welcome to our Gila Monster Information Site!!

Hello! Welcome to our Gila monster information page. Why do we have a site dedicated to theGila monsters? Cause Gila monsters are pretty awesome. For one thing, they're cute! But don'tget too close to a Gila monster. There's a reason the name sounds scary. If a Gila monster bites you, it's venom is poisonus. But Gila monsters aren't all bad. Scientists think their saliva mightcure diabetes and Alzheimer's Disease!

Click here to buy my handmade Gila monster jewelry!

I LOVE GILA MONSTERS

Click here to buy posters of the Gila monster!

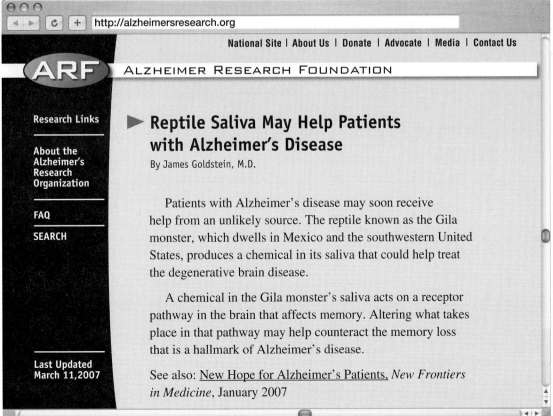

http://alzheimersresearch.org

National Site | About Us | Donate | Advocate | Media | Contact Us

ARF ALZHEIMER RESEARCH FOUNDATION

Research Links

About the Alzheimer's Research Organization

FAQ

SEARCH

▶ ## Reptile Saliva May Help Patients with Alzheimer's Disease

By James Goldstein, M.D.

Patients with Alzheimer's disease may soon receive help from an unlikely source. The reptile known as the Gila monster, which dwells in Mexico and the southwestern United States, produces a chemical in its saliva that could help treat the degenerative brain disease.

A chemical in the Gila monster's saliva acts on a receptor pathway in the brain that affects memory. Altering what takes place in that pathway may help counteract the memory loss that is a hallmark of Alzheimer's disease.

See also: New Hope for Alzheimer's Patients, *New Frontiers in Medicine*, January 2007

Last Updated March 11, 2007

Evaluating Web Sites, continued

1. What is the purpose of each site? Explain your answer.

_____

_____

2. Who wrote the material that appears on each site?

_____

_____

3. Which site is more likely to contain up-to-date information? Why?

_____

_____

4. How could you confirm the information on each site?

_____

_____

5. Which site looks more professional? Explain your answer.

_____

_____

6. Based on the two sites' URLs, which site is more reliable? Why?

_____

_____

7. Which site should a student use for a report on the role of animal research in medicine? List three reasons for your choice.

_____

_____

_____

_____

8. Using the site you chose, list two facts that the student could use in the report.

_____

_____

_____

_____

Practice Paraphrasing

Read the source material. Then paraphrase the important ideas.

At a Glance

To paraphrase:
- read the source carefully
- record important information in your own words and sentence patterns
- keep your paraphrase the same length as the original or a bit shorter.

Chicken Eggs Used in Production of Cancer Treatment

by Mischa Rosenwald Ph. D

Initial clinical trials have shown remarkable hope for skin cancer treatments derived from genetically modified chicken eggs. These chickens have been engineered to lay eggs that contain miR24, a type of antibody with potential for treating malignant melanoma, a form of skin cancer. These antibodies are given to genetically modify chickens so that their eggs contain the antibodies that fight cancer. After the chickens lay the eggs, the antibodies are removed through a simple procedure and prepared for use in drugs for cancer treatment.

_____

_____

_____

_____

_____

_____

_____

_____

_____

Cancer-Fighting Enzyme Found in Starfish Eggs

by Victor Lopez

A species of spiny starfish called the *Marthasterias glacialis*, found in the chilly waters of the English Channel, may be the latest weapon in the battle against cancer. The eggs of this starfish contain high levels of an enzyme that may be useful in new cancer treatments. Specifically, it could help to control the rapid cell division that results in tumors.

The enzyme is present in all animals. However, the spiny starfish eggs are by far the most plentiful source.

_____

_____

_____

_____

_____

_____

_____

_____

_____

New Breakthrough in Plant-Based Medicines

by Priya Mehtani

Scientists have long known that plant seeds can be used to make proteins that are similar to the antibodies the human body creates to fight diseases. But until recently, they could only make the proteins in small amounts.

Now, scientists at Ghent University in Belgium have managed to increase the yield of proteins from the *Arabidopsis* plant. Their work may lower the cost of producing antibodies used in treating hepatitis A and some forms of cancer.

_____

_____

_____

_____

_____

_____

_____

_____

_____

Chinese Remedy May Lead to Malaria Drug

by Nicholas Zumer

Malaria, one of the world's deadliest diseases, has always been difficult and costly to treat. But a new drug may make things much easier. The drug, called OZ227 or OZ, is based on an herbal medicine used in China that comes from a plant known as sweet wormwood.

Although the new medicine does not come from the same plant, it has a similar structure and attacks malaria in the same way. But there is one key difference: cost. Herbal medicines, produced by extracting chemicals from plants, are expensive to manufacture. Because it is man-made, OZ will be much cheaper to produce.

_____

_____

_____

_____

_____

_____

_____

_____

_____

_____

_____

Practice Summarizing

Read each article carefully. Then summarize it.

At a Glance

To summarize:

- read your source carefully

- restate the main ideas in your own words

- condense important details and examples, use headings that tell what the summary is about.

ASPIRIN

Aspirin is a drug taken to reduce pain or to bring down fevers. It has also been shown to reduce the risk of heart attacks for those who take it regularly.

Aspirin comes from salicylic acid. Salicylic acid is derived from a substance called salicin that is found in the bark of willow trees. Long before aspirin was developed, people used willow bark to relieve pain. Ancient Egyptians chewed willow bark as a remedy for fevers and headaches. Hippocrates, the ancient Greek physician, had patients chew willow bark to ease the pains of rheumatism.

In 1832, a German scientist used salicin to create salicylic acid. Later researchers were able to produce a pure, powdered form of salicylic acid, which led to the development of aspirin in 1899.

For years, it was thought that German chemist Felix Hoffmann was the first person to produce powdered salicylic acid in 1897. However, researchers now believe that Hoffmann's supervisor, Alfred Eichengrun, should be credited with the discovery.

Today, aspirin can be bought over the counter. It is one of the most popular drugs in the world. About 100 billion tablets are manufactured each year.

_____

_____

_____

_____

_____

_____

_____

_____

_____

_____

_____

Extra Garlic, Please!

by Shoshana Feinstein

June 1, 2007

Garlic may not be good for your breath, but it can be great for your health. Researchers believe the pungent bulb can help protect against serious medical conditions, such as cancer and high blood pressure, as well as minor maladies like the common cold.

A member of the lily family, garlic is best known as a sharp-tasting, onion-like herb. But people have long used it for purposes other than seasoning. Ancient Egyptians chewed garlic before long journeys, believing that the foul breath it gave them would protect them against evil spirits. In ancient Greece and Rome, soldiers and athletes ate garlic to increase their strength. Greek doctors prescribed garlic to treat wounds, digestive disorders, and heart ailments.

In medieval Europe, garlic was thought to help guard against the Black Plague. It was also used to treat many illnesses, including leprosy. A hardy, easily transportable plant, garlic was introduced to many countries around the world during the Renaissance. Later, during World War I, it was used to prevent soldiers' wounds from becoming infected.

Today, many medical practitioners recommend raw garlic or garlic supplements to treat everything from upset stomachs to ear infections. Experts also believe that chemicals found in garlic can lower blood cholesterol and help prevent heart disease.

Using Direct Quotes

On each index card, record an important quote from the article. Use ellipses or brackets as needed.

At a Glance

Follow these tips when you record quotes:

- use quotation marks to show where the quote begins and ends

- use ellipses (…) to show any places where you left words out

- use brackets [ ] around any words you changed.

All About Acupuncture

by Mark Marzano

One of the world's oldest medical procedures is becoming more popular in the United States today. Americans increasingly use acupuncture, a 2,000-year-old practice, to treat various medical conditions. The 2002 National Health Interview Survey found that over eight million American adults have tried acupuncture. Of these, one quarter had had acupuncture treatments within the past year.

Acupuncture has its roots in traditional Chinese medicine. Practitioners believe that energy flows through the body along pathways called meridians. Treating certain points on the body can improve this flow of energy. Acupuncture treatment involves using very thin needles to puncture the skin at these key points. Although the process may sound painful, it causes little or no pain when properly performed. Some studies show that acupuncture can help to relieve pain. Dr. Susan Cameron of the Alternative Therapies Institute says that acupuncture is usually most effective when combined with other treatments.

Record one good quote you plan to use in your research report.

_____

_____

_____

_____

Acupuncture—Popularity

"Americans increasingly use acupuncture …to treat various medical conditions."

Marzano, 46

Avoiding Plagiarism

Read the source and the student paper. Then edit the student paper to fix any plagiarism.

At a Glance

To avoid accidental plagiarism:

- use quotation marks around any text taken directly from a source
- use your own wording and sentence patterns when paraphrasing ideas
- give credit to the writer (or source) whenever you quote or paraphrase another writer's ideas.

Source

The Soothing Properties of Salt

by John McTighe

Most people know that eating too much salt is unhealthy, of course. But salt can actually be used to help relieve a number of minor health complaints.

For example, gargling several times a day with warm saltwater can ease a sore throat. Mix half a teaspoon of salt with eight ounces of warm water, then gargle with the solution to soothe inflamed tissues. Additionally, rinsing with different amounts of salt and warm water can help relieve aches in gums and teeth until you can get to a dentist's office. Warm saltwater can also help with the pain if you accidentally burn your mouth.

Student Paper

The Healing Qualities of Salt

As everyone knows, eating too much salt is not good for you. But salt can actually be used to help relieve a number of minor health complaints. For example, gargling three or four times per day with a warm saltwater solution can relieve the pain of a sore throat. You should mix a half-teaspoon of salt with eight ounces of water. Then gargle with the solution to soothe the swollen tissues in your throat. Rinsing with salt and warm water can also help with any pains in your teeth and gums until you get a chance to visit your dentist. Warm saltwater can also help with the pain if you accidentally burn your mouth.

Practice Synthesizing Ideas

Study the Inquiry Chart. Then write a synthesis of the information presented for each research question.

Research Questions	Source Information	Synthesis
What are the latest discoveries in the field of plant-based medicine?	Certain plant seeds can be used to make proteins that are similar to human antibodies (Mehtani 89). Recently, scientists increased the yield of proteins from the Arabidopsis plant (Mehtani 89). Scientists recently developed a drug called OZ27 that's similar to an herbal medicine used to treat malaria (Zumer 25).	_____ _____ _____ _____ _____ _____ _____ _____ _____ _____ _____ _____ _____ _____
How will the latest discoveries affect drug production?	The increased protein yield will make certain medicines much cheaper to produce (Mehtani 89). Herbal medicines, produced by extracting chemicals from plants, are expensive to manufacture (Zumer 25). Because it is made by humans, OZ27 is more expensive to produce than drugs extracted from plants (Zumer 25).	_____ _____ _____ _____ _____ _____ _____ _____ _____ _____ _____ _____ _____ _____

Check for Focus

Delete any information that doesn't relate to the research question. Then write a synthesis of the information.

Research Questions	Source Information	Synthesis
What was medical care like during the Civil War?	Most surgeons during the Civil War had never treated a gunshot wound before (Mitchell 25).	
	The Civil War began after 11 southern states left the Union (Papadakis 59).	
	Doctors prescribed what was available, from green vegetables for the disease known as scurvy to quinine for malaria (Drexell 302).	
	Houses, schools, and even barns were used as hospitals (Aster 83).	
	Jefferson Davis, the president of the new Confederacy, chose Robert E. Lee to lead the southern army (Rivera 65).	
	During the Civil War, doctors did not know what we know today about preventing the spread of germs (Mitchell 37).	

Develop an Outline

1 Write a draft of your outline for your research report:

- use roman numerals for the main topics in your paper
- use capital letters for ideas that will become the main ideas in your paragraphs
- use numbers for details.

219

Develop an Outline, continued

2 Now type your outline with correct indentation and paste it here.

Practice Good Introductions

Read this introduction from a research report.

Techniques for Good Introductions

- Show how your topic relates to your readers' experiences.
- Ask a question you plan to answer in your paper.
- Present an attention-getting fact, quotation, or anecdote.

Acupuncture: An Alternative Therapy

More and more people in the United States are turning to "alternative" medical treatments in addition to, or even instead of, traditional medicine. One of these alternative treatments is acupuncture which originated in China. Acupuncturists pierce the skin with metal needles. Some conditions that have been treated with acupuncture include headaches, tennis elbow, back pain, and even asthma.

Rewrite the introduction in three different ways, using each of the techniques to get readers' attention.

1. _____
_____
_____
_____
_____

2. _____
_____
_____
_____
_____

3. _____
_____
_____
_____
_____

Practice Good Introductions, continued

Draft two different versions of an introduction for your own research report.

1. _____

_____

_____

_____

_____

_____

_____

_____

_____

_____

_____

_____

2. _____

_____

_____

_____

_____

_____

_____

_____

_____

_____

_____

_____

_____

From Outline to Paragraphs

Use the outline to draft a paragraph for this report.

II. What is "pharming"?
   A. Term comes from "pharmaceuticals" (medicines)
   B. "Pharming" means genetically altering farm animals to produce substances used in medical treatments
   C. Could lead to new medical breakthroughs

_____

_____

_____

_____

_____

_____

_____

Use your outline from pages 219–220 to draft a paragraph for your research report.

_____

_____

_____

_____

_____

_____

_____

_____

_____

_____

_____

_____

_____

_____

_____

Practice Strong Conclusions

Read the thesis statement and concluding paragraph for each report. Then rewrite the paragraph to improve the conclusion.

Techniques for Strong Conclusions

- Clearly connect the ideas in the conclusion to the thesis of the paper.
- Leave the reader with something to remember, like a quote, a new question, or a solution to a problem.

Thesis: Simple things people buy in the grocery store can help solve health problems.

Expensive medicines are necessary sometimes. But we should not forget that simple things can also be good for health. Eating garlic can lower blood pressure and help guard against serious diseases like cancer and less serious ones like colds. It has also been used to treat wounds. You should not eat too much chocolate. But small amounts of dark chocolate can lower blood pressure and help prevent heart disease. Raspberries can help prevent some kinds of cancer. Many foods that are good for you are easy to find. Of course, it is important to practice other good health habits as well.

_____
_____
_____
_____
_____
_____
_____
_____
_____
_____
_____
_____
_____
_____